D0108276

The Idea of Race

The Idea of Race

by

Ashley Montagu

UNIVERSITY OF NEBRASKA PRESS · LINCOLN

Portions of this book were originally presented in the Montgomery Lectureship on Contemporary Civilization at the University of Nebraska.

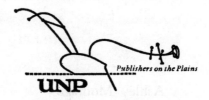

Publishers on the Plains

UNP

Manufactured in the United States of America

To
Harry Edmonds
Founder and Director
of
International House, New York,
And Happy Memories of
1927–1928, 1930–1931

Preface

The first two lectures in this volume were delivered as the Montgomery Lectures on Contemporary Civilization at the University of Nebraska, Lincoln, on the 7th and 8th of December, 1964. I am grateful to the University for the honor and the opportunity. The third lecture was written to round out the discussion of this always controversial subject. For the warm hospitality shown me by all my new friends in Lincoln, I can only say that it made not only the snow melt, but me too.

ASHLEY MONTAGU

Princeton, New Jersey

Contents

Contents

The Idea of Race

I.

Race: The History of an Idea

"He who degrades his fellow man to be a beggar
and a knave will always be the first to call him so."
—Heinrich Pestalozzi

INTRODUCTION

"Race" is a problem that has been very much
with the world during the twentieth century.
More, indeed, than in any other, and in our
own time certainly disturbingly more obtrusive
than at any previous period in our history. It
is a problem of the greatest seriousness in this
country, and in many other parts of the world
it has in recent years become explosive. It was
not always so. It comes as a great surprise to
most people to learn that the idea of "race" is
of very recent origin. The idea of "race" as a
widespread secular belief is, in fact, no older
than the nineteenth century. Because it is important in dealing with the Hydra-headed phenomenon of "race" to understand the history
of the development of that idea, and because

3

it properly, and, it is to be hoped, illuminat-
ingly, belongs at the commencement of our
inquiry, I shall devote this first part of our
discussion to a résumé of that history.

We shall discuss first the social idea of "race."
This will be followed by a discussion of the
biological idea of "race." These two separate
conceptions of "race" need to be carefully distinguished from one another, for the one is
general, popular, and widespread, and the other
passes as scientific. Unfortunately, these two
conceptions are usually confused with each
other.

The Social Idea of "Race"

When the members of a society act out their
emotions and beliefs in relation to the members of other groups in discriminatory ways,
based on a conception of the others which is
socially determined, we are clearly dealing with
a group distinction. Such is the social conception of "race." More specifically defined, the
social idea of "race" is the notion that there
exists a something called "race" that insep-

4

arably links two things together, namely, physical traits and behavioral traits. These traits are
said to be held in common heredity by distinc-
tive intrabreeding groups or populations. It is
held that just as this common heredity determines the physical characteristics of such
groups, so, too, it determines their behavioral
characteristics. Upon this view, not only are
physical and behavioral traits determined by
"race," but so are the collective achievements
of the peoples characterized by such traits.

The social idea of "race" has it, then, that
physical and behavioral traits are linked, and
that different kinds of linkages of this nature
characterize different peoples, thus accounting
for their physical and behavioral differences,
and that, finally, cultural achievement is determined by "race." Since, so the argument runs,
there are differences in the hereditary poten-
tials of such different groups, it is these hereditary differences that are largely, if not entirely,
responsible for the differences in cultural
achievement exhibited by the different "races."

This kind of interpretation of the differences

5

presented by different groups represents not only the easiest explanation of the observed differences, but also the most comforting to those who indulge in it. It is an easy and obvious sort of interpretation of the existing differences. The easiest and most obvious explanation, however comforting it may be, is not thereby rendered the correct explanation. Appearances are deceptive. The obvious is neither necessarily true nor right. Indeed, there is only one thing wrong with the social conception of "race," and that is that it goes beyond the facts, that it is, in fact, quite in conflict with the facts, that it is, in short, in error. As such, as we shall see, the social idea of "race" represents a collection of pseudological rationalizations based on a confusion of emotions, prejudiced judgments, and disordered values.

It is because the idea of "race," and especially the social conception of "race," is so anti-human and individually and socially destructive that it demands our most earnest attention.

The Biological Idea of "Race"

The biological idea of "race," that is, the idea of "race" to which biologists in general subscribe and which until recently they universally took for granted, is that there exist subdivisions of species, that is, populations of a species, capable of interbreeding with one another and characterized by hereditary differences in certain physical or physiological traits. The biological conception of "race" is extended to man by most biologists and physical anthropologists. As applied both to man and to other animals, however, that conception has in recent years come under some criticism from biologists and physical anthropologists. Since these criticisms have raised serious questions concerning the reality of anything corresponding to a biological "race," especially with reference to man, we shall devote some attention to that idea also.

Origin of the Idea of "Race"

The origin of the word "race" is obscure. Attempts have been made to derive it from the Arabic *ras*; the Latin *ratio*, meaning order,

7

or the Latin *radix*, meaning a root; the Italian *razza*; and the Spanish and Portuguese *raza*. The first use of the word in printed English is to be found in the second English edition of the martyrologist John Foxe's *Actes and Monuments*, popularly known as the *Book of Martyrs*, published in 1570. In this work Foxe writes, "Thus was the outward race & stock of Abraham after flesh refused."[1] But this is a rather special use of the term, referring to the offspring or posterity of a person. In the sense of a tribe, nation, or people descended from a common stock, the first English usage of the term is to be found in Wynne's *History of the Gwydir Family*, published in 1600, where the author refers to "Llewelyn ap Gruffith last Prince of Wales of the Brittish race."[2] In the sense of a breed or stock of animals or a particular variety of a species, the first English usage occurs in Blundeville's *Horsemanship*, pub-

[1] John Foxe, *Actes and Monuments* (1570), II, 1841.
[2] Wynne of Gwydir, *History of the Gwydir Family* (1600), p. 20.

8

lished in 1580.[3] In the sense of one of the major groups of mankind having certain physical traits in common, the earliest English usage occurs in Oliver Goldsmith's *The Natural History of Animals*, which appeared in 1774, and in which he writes, "The second great variety in the human species seems to be that of the Tartar race."[4] In France, François Taut, in his book entitled *Trésor de la langue française*, published in 1600, derived the word from the Latin *radix*, and stated that "it alludes to the extraction of a man, of a dog, of a horse; as one says of good or bad race."[5]

It is clear, then, that the word "race" was already in use in the sixteenth century in the sense of a group or population having certain physical traits in common. While there are no significant references to the fact in the contemporary literature, there can be little doubt

[3] Thomas Blundeville, *The Fower Chiefest Offices Belonging to Horsemanship* (1580).

[4] Oliver Goldsmith, *An History of the Earth and Animated Nature* (London: J. Nourse, 1774), p. xxxiii.

[5] François Taut, *Trésor de la langue française*, ed. Jean Nicot (Paris: P. Doucer, 1600).

that the physical distinctions that were recognized to exist between different individuals of different populations were sometimes associated with behavioral peculiarities. It is quite clear, though, that nothing resembling the modern idea of "race" existed as either a social, a political, or as a scientific viewpoint.

In the eighteenth century there were some who took it for granted that the differences, both physical and mental, that distinguished whites from Negroes were inborn. It was not, however, until the latter part of the eighteenth century, with the beginning of the debate which eventually lead to the abolition of the trade in slaves and to their ultimate emancipation, that the alleged inborn differences between peoples were erected into the doctrine of racism. This doctrine constituted a mélange of rationalizations calculated to prove that the Negro was created with articulate speech and hands so that he might be of service to his master, the white man. There were many people who quite honestly believed in the Negro's inferiority, reasoning that their illiteracy and degraded condition

10

was due to their inborn inadequacies. Thomas Jefferson, for example, originally thought Negroes poor in mental endowment, but believed in their emancipation, with the qualification that when freed they were "to be removed beyond the reach of mixture."[6] This statement is often quoted by racists and others who neglect, however, to add that with increased experience of Negroes Jefferson later several times repudiated his earlier opinions. In 1792, in a letter to Benjamin Banneker, the Negro slave-born inventor and mathematician, praising the latter's *Almanac*, Jefferson wrote how much he welcomed "such proofs as you exhibit that nature has given to our black brethren talents equal to those of the other colors of men, and that the appearance of a want of them is owing merely to the degraded condition of their existence. . . ."[7]

Some seventeen years later, in 1809, Jefferson

[6] Thomas Jefferson, "Notes on the State of Virginia," in Saul K. Padover (ed.), *The Complete Jefferson* (New York: Tudor Publishing Co., 1943), p. 662.

[7] Philip S. Foner, *Basic Writings of Thomas Jefferson* (New York: Halcyon House, 1950), p. 601.

11

wrote, "Be assured that no person living wishes more sincerely than I do to see a complete refutation of the doubts I have myself entertained and expressed on the grade of understanding allotted to them [Negroes] by nature, and to find that in this respect they are on a par with ourselves. My doubts were the result of personal observation on the limited sphere of my own State, where the opportunities for the development of their genius were not favorable, and those of exercising it still less so. I expressed them therefore with great hesitation; but whatever be their degree of talent is no measure of their rights."[8]

Finally, there is Jefferson's ringing comment, "The mass of mankind has not been born with saddles on their back, nor a favored few booted and spurred, ready to ride them legitimately, by the grace of God."[9]

In antiquity the Egyptians, the Jews, the Greeks, and the Romans, whatever distinctions

[8] *Ibid.*, p. 682.
[9] Saul K. Padover, *A Jefferson Profile* (New York: John Day, 1956), p. 344.

they made between themselves and others, even though they recognized the obvious physical differences, seldom or never based those distinctions on racial grounds. St. Paul's dictum, "God hath made of one blood all nations of men for to dwell on all the face of the earth" (Acts 17:26), was an advance upon the Greek way of viewing the world as divided into themselves and barbarians. However, the Greeks, though they affected to despise the barbarian, did so on cultural grounds, and never on anything resembling racial grounds. The Greeks thought of Hellenism as a thing of the spirit rather than of "race." As Isocrates (436–338 B.C.) wrote, "So far has Athens distanced the rest of mankind in thought and in speech that her pupils have become the teachers of the rest of the world; and she has brought it about that the name 'Hellenes' is applied rather to those who share our culture than to those who share a common blood."[10]

[10] Isocrates *Panegyricus* iv. 50; trans. by George Norlin (Loeb Classical Library; Cambridge: Harvard University Press, 1928), I, pp. xxiv, 149.

13

It is perfectly true that in Greece and in Rome suggestions were sometimes made concerning inherent differences between people, but this idea never gained a firm foothold at any time.

Aristotle is sometimes referred to as having held views on the biological inequality of "races." This is not true. Aristotle, like many another, has been misquoted and misrepresented. Aristotle's views were clearly stated, and they refer to the natural inequalities that exist between individuals in the *same* society primarily, and only secondarily to differences which separated the Greeks from other peoples, or barbarians.

Since Aristotle's views played a considerable role in the development of what ultimately became the idea of "race," we may briefly consider what he wrote.

In the *Politics* (Bk. I, Chap. 5) Aristotle wrote, "Ruling and being ruled, which is the relation of master and slave, not only belongs to the category of things necessary, but also to that of things expedient; and there are species

14

in which a distinction is already marked, immediately at birth, between those of its members who are intended for being ruled and those who are intended to rule" (# 2). "We may thus conclude that all men who differ from others as much as the body differs from the soul, or an animal from a man (and this is the case with all those whose function is bodily service, and who produce their best when they supply such service)—all such are by nature slaves, and it is better for them, on the very same principle as in the other cases just mentioned, to be ruled by a master" (# 8). "A man is thus by nature a slave if he is capable of becoming (and this is the reason why he also actually becomes) the property of another, and if he participates in reason to the extent of apprehending it in another, though destitute of it himself" (# 9).

Aristotle goes on, "We have hitherto been speaking of mental differences. But it is nature's intention also to erect a physical difference between the body of the freeman and that of the slave, giving the latter strength for the menial duties of life, but making the former upright in carriage and (though useless for physical labour) useful for the various purposes of civic life" (# 10).

Finally, in a famous paragraph, Aristotle concludes, "It is thus clear that, just as some are by nature free, so others are by nature slaves, and for these latter the condition of slavery is both beneficial and just" (# 125a).[11]

Reading Aristotle carefully, it is quite evident that his approach, as Westermann says, "was entirely from the political-economic point of view," and applies to Greeks as well as to all other peoples.[12] What Aristotle was saying, in short, was that there exist natural differences between individuals, *not* between peoples, and that it is these natural, and in some cases cultural, differences that determine the relations of individuals to one another. The cultural differences existing between peoples that enable

[11] Aristotle *Politics* i. Chap. 5, in *The Politics of Aristotle*, trans. and ed. by Ernest Barker (Oxford: Clarendon Press, 1946).

[12] W. L. Westermann, "The Slave Systems of Greek and Roman Antiquity," *Memoirs of the American Philosophical Society*, XL (1955), xi–180.

16

the superior to subjugate the inferior not only entitle but justify the superior in enslaving the inferior. Thus, Aristotle writes, " 'Slavery' and 'slave' are terms which are used in two different senses. There is, as we have seen, a kind of slavery which exists by nature; but there is also a kind of slave, and of slavery, which exists only by law or (to speak more exactly) convention. (The law in virtue of which those vanquished in war are held to belong to the victor is in effect a sort of convention)." And, Aristotle concludes, "The superior *in goodness* ought to rule over, and be the master of, his inferiors."[13]

If Aristotle had any biologistic or racial ideas, he never clearly expressed them. It is surely not without significance that his pupil Alexander the Great expressed himself unreservedly and unequivocally upon the unity of man. As Tarn says, "Alexander believed that he had a mission from the deity to harmonize men generally and be reconciler of the world, mixing men's lives and customs as in a loving cup . . . to bring about, as between mankind generally, *Homo-*

[13] Aristotle *Politics* i. Chap. 6.

17

neia and peace and fellowship and make them all one people. . . . Plutarch makes him say that God is the common father of all mankind."[14]

Whatever Aristotle may originally have had in mind, subsequent generations have interpreted his words as they wished and laid the ground for what was eventually to become a racist interpretation of history and government.

Jean Jacques Rousseau's resounding reply to Aristotle brilliantly presents the Enlightenment view. "Aristotle said," writes Rousseau, "that men were not naturally equal, but that some were born for slavery, and others for domination. Aristotle was right, but he took the effect for the cause. Nothing can be more certain than that every man born in slavery is born for slavery. Slaves lose everything in their chains, even the desire to escape from them; they love servitude as the companions of Ulysses loved their brutish condition. If then, there are slaves by nature, it is because there have been slaves

[14] W. W. Tarn, *Alexander the Great and the Unity of Mankind* (London, 1933), pp. 3, 7, 21, 28.

against nature. Force made the first slaves, and their cowardice perpetuated them."[15]

It is not to be supposed that there were not in earlier times men who accounted for the behavioral differences between peoples on biological grounds. Inherent causes were certainly offered as an explanation of such differences on more than one occasion. However, such explanations simply made no headway against the criticism to which they were exposed. For example, the great fourteenth-century Arab scholar Ibn Khaldûn (1332–1406), in his work *The Muqaddimah* (1337) writes, "Al-Mas'ûdî undertook to investigate the reason for the levity, excitability, and emotionalism in Negroes, and attempted to explain it. However, he did no better than to report, on the authority of Galen and Ya'qûb b. Ishâq al-Kindi, that the reason is a weakness of their brains which results in a weakness of their intellect." Upon this Ibn

[15] Jean Jacques Rousseau, "The Social Contract," in *A Discourse on the Origin of Inequality* and *The Social Contract*, trans. by G. D. H. Cole (Everyman's Library; New York: E. P. Dutton, 1932), Bk. I, Chap. 2.

Khaldûn remarks, "This is an inconclusive and unproven statement. 'God guides whomever he wants to guide.'"[16] Ibn Khaldûn's own explanation of the Negro's high spirits is entirely environmental, attributing them largely to climatic factors.

One sometimes finds it stated in the literature—and what is even worse, the statements are made as if they were direct quotations from the original sources—that certain writers in antiquity did clearly point to the biological differences as explanatory of the behavioral differences between peoples. One of the most widely diffused of these statements occurs in Ruth Benedict's book *Race: Science and Politics*. In this excellent book Cicero is quoted as writing to his friend Atticus, "Do not obtain your slaves from Britain, because they are so stupid and so utterly incapable of being taught that they are not fit to form part of the house-

[16] Ibn Khaldûn, *The Muqaddimah*, trans. and ed. by Franz Rosenthal (New York: Pantheon Books, 1958), Vol. I, Bk. 1, pp. 175–176.

hold of Athens."[17] Unhappily, Cicero made no such derogatory remark. It could be wished that he had. What he actually wrote was ". . . there is not a scrap of silver in the island, nor any hope of booty except from slaves; but I don't fancy you will find any with literary or musical talent among them."[18]

Cicero was wrong. The talents were there, both silver and genetic, but it took more than a thousand years before the genetic talents began to find expression. This long period of cultural lag in spite of the presence of the Romans in Britain for more than four centuries is worth reflecting upon.

And what of the Greeks in the second millennium B.C.? Who were they? A few hardworking illiterate peasant peoples attempting to wrest a living from the soil. And in the sixth century B.C. who were the Romans? Several

[17] Ruth Benedict, *Race: Science and Politics* (New York: Viking Press, 1943), p. 10.
[18] Cicero *Letters to Atticus*, trans. and ed. by E. O. Winstedt (Loeb Classical Library; Cambridge: Harvard University Press, 1920), I, 324.

thousand poor farmers scattered over the seven hills by the Tiber. What warrant was there in the food-grubbing peasants of these Mediterranean lands for the promise they subsequently so richly realized? And yet from these unkempt lowly farmers was to emerge the two most highly developed civilizations the world has known, the civilizations to which the Western world owes virtually everything it calls its own.

Who could have foretold that from these lowly peoples would emerge a Socrates, a Plato, an Aristotle, an Archimedes, a Euclid, an Aristophanes, a Euripides, a Pindar, a Pericles, a Solon, a Marcus Aurelius, an Ovid, a Catullus, a Lucretius, to name but a few? Who could have foretold that from those barbaric Britons of Cicero's day, more than fifteen hundred years later a Shakespeare would be born, a Ben Jonson, a John Donne, a Christopher Marlowe, a Gilbert of Rochester, a Bacon?

Peoples, like individuals, it would seem, require time and opportunities in which to realize their potentialities.

But we run somewhat ahead. How did the

modern idea of "race" get started? It started, interestingly enough, in the Catholic church. In the year 1455 Pope Nicholas V, by decree, approved the subjugation of infidels to Christians.[19] The immediate result of this decree was the conversion of a religious-social difference into a socioeconomic, but not yet a "racial," discrimination. The decree meant that official sanction had been given to the enslavement of Negroes, Indians, and other "infidels" so that salvation of their souls and their entrance into God's Kingdom could be assured. It is from this time, the year 1455, that the Portuguese trade in slaves, principally in Africa, began in earnest.

Writing a hundred years later, the historian Joao de Barros states that the church gave the Portuguese a free hand to make war without provocation on non-Christian peoples, to reduce them into slavery, and to seize their lands, since they were "unjust possessors of them."[20]

[19] Anne Fremantle (ed.), *The Papal Encyclicals* (New York: New American Library, 1963), p. 77.

[20] Quoted in Lewis Hanke, *Aristotle and the American Indians* (Chicago: Henry Regnery Co., 1959), p. 108.

As Lewis Hanke states, "The infidel, in the eyes of the Portuguese, had neither rights of property nor personal rights. The salvation of his soul justified the loss of his personal liberty."[21]

In March 1493 Christopher Columbus was forced to land in Portugal, and King John II maintained that the papal bull *Romanus Pontifex*, 8 January 1455, which granted the territories discovered in Africa to Portugal, also included America. Ferdinand and Isabella of Spain protested, whereupon Pope Alexander VI issued three bulls, the most important of which, *Inter Caetera Divinae* (1493), encouraged the Spanish monarchs "to subdue the said mainlands and islands, and their natives and inhabitants, with God's grace, and to bring them to the Catholic faith."[22]

In his letter of March 1493 to Ferdinand and Isabella, Columbus remarks on the great friendliness of the Indians and of their "excellent and acute understanding." But to the rulers and their minions whose cupidity had been aroused,

[21] *Ibid.*
[22] Fremantle, *The Papal Encyclicals*, p. 77.

24

this was of no interest. The moment of magnificence was forever lost, and soon the shameful expropriation and destruction of the Indians, who resisted enslavement, began. On 29 May 1537 Pope Paul III issued the bull *Pastorale officium*, condemning the enslavement of Indians, declaring it heresy to say that they were irrational and incapable of conversion. The Pope also tried to transfer spiritual authority over the Indians from the Spanish Inquisition, which was controlled by the Spanish crown, to the bishop, but without success. It is worth quoting the significant part of the bull of 1537:

It has come to our hearing that our very dear son in Christ, Charles, the ever august Emperor of the Romans who is also king of Castile and Aragon, anxious to check those who, burning with avarice, possess an inhuman spirit, has prohibited all his subjects by public edict from bringing the Western and Southern Indians into slavery, or daring to deprive them of their possessions. These Indians therefore, although they live outside the bosom of the Church, nevertheless have not been, nor are they to be, deprived of their freedom of ownership of their own possessions, since they are human beings and, consequently, capable of faith and salvation. They are not to be destroyed by slavery, but to be invited to life by preaching and example. Furthermore, desiring to repress the shameful deeds of such wicked men and to ensure that the Indians are not alienated by injuries and punishments so that they find it more difficult to embrace the faith of Christ, we lay it as a charge and a command by this present letter upon your Circumspection—in whose righteousness, foresight, zeal and experience in these matters and in others we have in the Lord special trust—that either by your own action or by that of others you provide to all the aforesaid Indians the help of an effective defence in the matters referred to previously; and we enjoin that you very strictly forbid all and sundry of whatever dignity, position, condition, rank and excellence, to bring the above-said Indians into slavery in any way or to dare to deprive them of their possessions in any manner under pain, if they do so, of incurring thereby excommunication "latae sententiae," from which they can only be absolved by ourselves or the Roman Pontiff reigning at the time, except if they are at the point of death and have previously made amends.[23]

[23] *Ibid.*, pp. 80–81.

Charles was so troubled in conscience by the behavior of his subjects to the Indians that he later suspended all expeditions to America while he sought to determine how to carry on the conquest of the Americas in a Christian manner. Toward this end, and under the powerful influence of that extraordinary man Bartolomé de Las Casas (1476–1566), friend of the Indians, he called together a junta, in the year 1550, of the leading theologians, jurists, and counselors to listen to a debate between Las Casas and the Spanish jurist Juan Gines de Sepulveda in order to determine the best way of dealing with the Indians. As Hanke remarks, "Probably never before has a mighty emperor . . . ordered his conquests to cease until it was decided if they were just."[24]

The great debate between Las Casas and Sepulveda was held in the capital at Valladolid. What was at issue was the Aristotelian claim that some men were born to be slaves and others to be their masters. Las Casas and others

[24] *Aristotle and the American Indians*, p. 37.

27

rejected this idea; Sepulveda argued in defense of it.

Forty years earlier, a Scottish scholar, John Major, in a book published in 1510, had been the first to apply the Aristotelian doctrine of natural slavery to the Indians.[25] A year later, on the island of Hispaniola in the Caribbean, a Dominican friar, Antonio de Montesinos, preached a remarkable sermon on the text "I am a voice crying in the wilderness," condemning his countrymen's treatment of the Indians and inquiring, "Are these Indians not men? Do they not have rational souls? Are you not obliged to love them as you love yourselves?"[26]

The reverberations of that sermon were not long in making themselves felt in Spain. Almost immediately a dispute arose at Burgos, where the first two works on Indian problems soon appeared, together with the publication of the first code setting out the manner in which

[25] John Major, *In primu Sententiarum* (Paris: J. Badi, 1510).

[26] Quoted in Hanke, *Aristotle and the American Indians*, pp. 14, 15.

Indians should be treated. One of these works, by the Dominican friar Matias de Paz, *Concerning the Rule of the Kings of Spain over the Indians*, represents not only the first study of its kind by a member of his order, but also the first known statement that the American Indians are not slaves in the Aristotelian sense.[27] This whole subject is admirably explored by Lewis Hanke in his *Aristotle and the American Indians.*

Las Casas, as early as 1519, when he was forty-five years of age and had had much experience in America, had already clashed with the Bishop of Darien, Juan Quevedo, on the merits of the Aristotelian doctrine. In 1545 Sepulveda had written a manuscript, under the auspices of the president of the Council of the Indies, seeking to show that wars against the Indians were just and even necessary to secure their conversion to Christianity. Sepulveda took as his principal task the demonstration of Aristotle's doctrine of natural slavery. He argued that it was neces-

[27] *Ibid.*, p. 15.

sary and lawful to wage war against the Indians
for four reasons: (1) for the gravity of the sins
which the Indians had committed, especially
their idolatries and their sins against nature;
(2) because of the rudeness of their natures,
which obliged them to serve persons having a
more refined nature, such as the Spaniards; (3)
in order to spread the faith, which would be
more easily accomplished by the prior subjugation of the Indians; and (4) to protect the weak
among the Indians themselves.

Sepulveda, who had never set foot in America, and if he had seen an Indian could have
done so only at some distance removed, was
forced to rely for his knowledge of the capacities
and achievements of Indians entirely upon
hearsay. This enabled him to declare that Indians were as inferior "as children are to adults,
as women are to men. Indians are as different
from Spaniards as cruel people are from mild
peoples." "How can we doubt," he asks, "that
these people, so uncivilized, so barbaric, so con-
taminated with so many sins and obscenities . . .
have been justly conquered by such an excel-

lent, pious, and most just king as was Ferdinand the Catholic and as is now Emperor Charles, and by such a humane nation which is excellent in every kind of virtue?"

These inferior people "require, by their own nature and in their own interests, to be placed under the authority of civilized and virtuous princes or nations, so that they may learn, from the might, wisdom, and law of their conquerors, to practice better morals, worthier customs, and more civilized ways of life."[28]

Sepulveda does not present a wholly racial or biologistic view of the differences between Indian and Spaniard, although something of that was undoubtedly implicit in what he intended to convey in the phrase "by the rudeness of their natures." It was a view which utterly outraged Las Casas.

"Mankind is one," declared Las Casas, "and all men are alike in that which concerns their creation and all natural things, and no one is born enlightened. From this it follows that all

[28] *Ibid.*, p. 15.

of us must be guided and aided at first by those who were born before us. And the savage peoples of the earth may be compared to uncultivated soil that readily brings forth weeds and useless thorns, but has within itself such natural virtue that by labour and cultivation it may be made to yield sound and beneficial fruits."[29]

In 1573, six years after the death of Las Casas, a general ordinance was passed regulating all future conquests and instituting many laws in behalf of the Indians. Thus, the spirit of Las Casas had finally achieved something of a victory. But the debate begun in Valladolid has never ended, and something more than its echoes are today heard in every part of the world.

During the seventeenth century increasing contact with the American Indians by the white settlers, and the purchase of Negroes as indentured servants, together with the subsequent institutionalization of Negro slavery in America toward the end of the century, served to pro-

[29] *Ibid.*

duce those conditions which in general favored the view that Aristotle was right, that some men were born to be slaves and some to be their masters. But, once again, this viewpoint was socioeconomic in origin and nature and not biologistic, although biologistic overtones could sometimes be detected.

With the growth of Negro slavery in America and the profitable trade in slaves, eighteenth-century America was firmly established in a system of legalized and other social rationalizations designed to make everyone feel comfortable with the institution of slavery. But these social devices were based virtually entirely on the view that since the Negro was a benighted heathen, unable to read or write, and belonging to a class and caste clearly inferior to those of his masters, his proper condition was that of a lifetime servant to his masters. To them, his masters, the slave would be making payment, in his servitude, for the privilege of protection and having his soul saved in the bargain. It was a great benison conferred by the slaveholders upon their slaves. Wealth and the ownership of slaves being a mark of divine grace, the proper place of the man of grace was in his mansion, while the slave stood at his gate. Each according to his divinely appointed station.

It was in 1670, fifty-one years after the purchase of "19 Negars" from a Portuguese man-of-war, that Virginia passed the law specifying "that all servants not being christians" who had been brought into the colony by sea were to be slaves for life. There was very little, if anything, in any of this of biologism or racism. The slaves were clearly different in every way from their masters, and because they were inferior, it was to the advantage of everyone, even to the slaves themselves, for them to be put under the protection of those who were able to exploit such of their talents as would render them most useful.

While the seeds of racism were being sown by such doctrines in the fertile soil of America, the poisonous plant was not to blossom until it had been intensively watered by the mainstream of ideas generated by the responses to the challenges of the Enlightenment, the Age

34

of Reason. The eighteenth century was the Century of the Rediscovery of Man. The voyages of exploration of Bougainville (1761–1766), of Wallis-Carteret (1766), of Captain Cook (1768–1779), and of many others had revealed the existence of hitherto undreamed-of varieties of man who, far from being the savages of popular imagination, turned out to be gentle and in many ways distinctly superior to their discoverers. Romantic ideas of a Golden Age, the deductions of philosophers, and the discoveries of explorers in an age that not only was ready to, but already was taking a new look at man, seeing him bold and clear, almost literally for the first time, gave men furiously to think and revalue some of their most cherished values. Added to this was the atmosphere of revolution; the challenge of new ideas; the criticism of authority, intolerance, superstition, and the constraints under which so many human beings were forced to live. The American and French Revolutions put the principles of "Life, Liberty, and the Pursuit of Happiness," of "Liberty, Fraternity, and Equality," squarely

35

before the world. The intellectual ferment that had precipitated these political upheavals, and of which perhaps the noblest product was the Declaration of Independence, drafted by the most eminent American luminary of the Enlightenment, Thomas Jefferson, soon expressed itself in the growth of the movement to abolish, as a first step, the trade in slaves.

Eighteenth-century scientific students of the variety of mankind were to a man all on the side of equality. Johann Friedrich Blumenbach, in the treatise that had created the science of physical anthropology, *On the Natural Variety of Mankind*, published in 1775, had written, "Although there seems to be so great a difference between widely separate nations, that you might easily take the inhabitants of the Cape of Good Hope, the Greenlanders, and the Circassians for so many different species of man, yet when the matter is thoroughly considered, you see that all do so run into one another, and that one variety of mankind does so sensibly pass into the other, that you cannot mark out the limits between them. Very arbitrary indeed

36

both in number and definition have been the varieties of mankind accepted by eminent men."[30]

Johann Gottfried Herder, in his great work *Outlines of a Philosophy of the History of Man*, published in four volumes from 1784 to 1791, wrote in startlingly modern terms:

> I could wish the distinctions between the human species, that have been made from a laudable zeal for discriminating science, not carried beyond due bounds. Some for instance have thought fit to employ the term *races* for four or five divisions, originally made in consequence of country or complexion but I see no reason for this appellation. Race refers to a difference of origin, which in this case does not exist, or in each of these countries, and under each of these complexions, comprises the most different races. . . . In short, there are neither four or five races, nor exclusive varieties, on this Earth. Complexions run into each other: forms follow the genetic character:

[30] Johann Friedrich Blumenbach, *De generis humani varietate nativa* (Göttingen, 1775); trans. by Thomas Bendyshe, *The Anthropological Treatises of Johann Friedrich Blumenbach* (London: Anthropological Society, 1865), pp. 98–99.

and upon the whole, all are at last but shades of the same great picture, extending through all ages, and over all parts of the Earth. They belong not, therefore, so properly to systematic natural history, as to the physico-geographical history of man.[31]

Much the same views were expressed by Buffon,[32] Rousseau,[33] the Humboldt brothers,[34] and many other scientific writers.[35]

[31] Johann Gottfried Herder, *Ideen zur Philosophie der Geschichte der Menschheit* (Riga and Leipzig: J. F. Hartknoch, 1784–1791); trans. by Thomas Churchill, *Outlines of a Philosophy of the History of Man* (London: J. Johnson, 1803), p. 298.

[32] Georges Louis Leclerc Buffon, *Histoire Naturelle* (Paris, 1749–1804); trans. by William Smellie, *Natural History* (London: Cadell & Davies, 1812), III, 302 ff.

[33] Jean Jacques Rousseau, "A Discourse on the Origin of Inequality," in *A Discourse on the Origin of Inequality* and *The Social Contract*, trans. by G. D. H. Cole (Everyman's Library; New York: E. P. Dutton, 1932), pp. 155–246.

[34] Alexander von Humboldt, *Cosmos: A Sketch of a Physical Description of the Universe*, trans. by E. C. Otté (London: Bohn, 1849); Wilhelm von Humboldt, *Über die Kawi-Sprache auf der Insel Java* (Berlin: Königlichen Akademie der Wissenschaften, 1836), Vol. III, p. 426.

[35] M. F. Ashley Montagu, *Man's Most Dangerous Myth: The Fallacy of Race* (4th ed.; Cleveland and New York: World Publishing Co., 1964).

What happened? How did it come about that the ideas reflected by such thinkers were virtually forgotten in the nineteenth century? The answer is that as a result of the pressures of rapidly changing socioeconomic conditions in the nineteenth century, such ideas were rapidly submerged under the avalanche of reactionary shibboleths.

The growing challenges of the abolitionists could evoke only the response from the defenders of slavery that the institution was justified. Since it was the scientific writers who had raised the biological issue, the defense now took the form, for the first time, of an explanation of the differences between the slaves and their masters based on biology. The Negro, it was now argued, was naturally, biologically, inferior to the white man.

It was in this manner that the doctrine of "race" was born. Burgeoning imperialism battened on such ideas as "superannuated races," "the white man's burden," "the lesser breeds without the law," "the Yellow Peril," "East is East and West is West/ And never the twain

39

shall meet," and other such notions. Indeed, if the idea of "race" had not already been available, the imperialists would have been forced to invent it. It was the most useful ideological instrument of all, even more valuable than the machine gun.

Darwinism was interpreted to mean that in the struggle for existence there was a competition between races in which the fittest, the superior, replaced the weakest, the inferior. In this way warfare between the races was justified because it rendered a biologically just decision. And what could be more neat than that.

By the middle of the nineteenth century the issue in America was squarely joined, leading eventually to open conflict between the North and the South—a conflict which has never ceased, a conflict which will not be settled on the battlefield, but in the consciences of men. Upon its outcome America as a power in the world will either stand or fall.

The issue of "race" is no longer a local one. It is more than an American problem: it is a problem which has now assumed world dimensions, in the Americas, Africa, Australia, Malaysia, Melanesia, Europe, and Asia. For this reason it has become more than ever the moral obligation of every self-respecting human being to make himself acquainted with the facts and the theories relating to the problems of "race" so that he may be able to think as clearly and act as intelligently as he should in relation to the most critical problem facing humanity today— the problem, no less, of humanity itself, which, alas, too many people among us see as the problem of "race."

II.
The Inequality of Man

"As man advances in civilization, and small tribes are united into larger communities, the simplest reason would tell each individual that he ought to extend his social instincts and sympathies to all members of the same nation, though personally unknown to him. This point being once reached, there is only an artificial barrier to prevent his sympathies extending to the men of all nations and races."—Charles Darwin, *The Descent of Man* (2d ed., 1875), p. 187.

BIOLOGICAL AND POLITICAL EQUALITY

It has always been evident that no two human beings, with the exception of identical twins, are ever born alike. When the signatories to the Declaration of Independence agreed to the words "All men are created equal," they meant not that all men were created biologically equal, but that they were created with equal rights to development; that "they are endowed by their Creator with certain unalienable rights; that among these are life, liberty, and the pursuit of happiness."

43

The claim for equality has never been a claim to equality of abilities, but a claim to the right of a man to share in the freedom to live and fulfill himself as a human being. It has never been in the least based on any idea of a biological equality of traits. Indeed, the idea of biological equality is nonsensical, and is, in any event, wholly irrelevant to the right of political equality.

In part because of that phrase "All men are created equal," and, of course, because of all those other conditions that bound them to support the institution, the defenders of slavery felt it necessary to show that the Negro was biologically unequal to the white man, both in his physical traits and in his mental capacities. As I have already pointed out, it was in this way that the doctrine of racism was born.

RACISM

The doctrine of racism combines both the biologistic and the social views of "race." Racism maintains that the visible physical hereditary differences that certain peoples exhibit,

44

and which distinguish them from other peoples, are inseparably linked with certain hereditarily determined behavioral traits. It is an essential tenet of this viewpoint that these hereditarily determined traits, especially with reference to behavior, differ significantly between these peoples, called "races," and are responsible for the differences in the learning capacities and achievements which distinguish one "race" from another.

This is the biologistic racist argument. From it the social racist argument follows. That argument is that since—and it is taken for granted that it is so—the behavioral differences between the "races" are for the most part biologically determined, it is desirable to make certain "racial" arrangements designed to achieve the following ends: (1) to prevent "homogenization" or "mongrelization," and thus deterioration of the superior "race"; (2) to keep the "races" segregated so that each has the opportunity to pursue "life, liberty, and happiness" within the prescribed limits; and (3) to provide educational and social opportunities for the members of

45

each "race" according to the limits of their as-
signed capacities, the "superior race," of course,
enjoying superior opportunities to those of
which the "inferior race" is held to be capable
of taking advantage.

The racist viewpoint has it that the biologically determined differences between the
"races" not only justify but require discriminatory arrangements in the conduct of the superior toward the alleged inferior "race." This,
furthermore, it is held, is desirable for both
"races." It is argued, for example, that it is un-
fair to both "races" to put them both into the
same classroom, for this on the one hand slows
up the learning of the members of the superior
"race," and on the other hand puts too heavy a
burden upon the members of the inferior
"race," and so on. The charity, consideration,
and thoughtfulness of the superior for the inferior "race" is sometimes quite touching!

RATIONALIZATIONS

These are, of course, the most canting of
rationalizations. Rationalizations have, how-

46

THE INEQUALITY OF MAN

ever, always proved serviceable substitutes for reasoning. Indeed, a comfortable rationalization usually appeals more strongly to most men than a calmly reasoned cold conclusion.

Rationalization is the process of concocting plausible reasons to account for one's practices or beliefs when these are challenged. Usually the rationalizer is unaware of the fact that he is attempting to justify his beliefs and practices with explanations that are unconnected with his true motivations; he is usually convinced that he is giving the true grounds for his beliefs. The rationalization is usually the easiest and most economical explanation, and since it appears to be reasonable and is emotionally satisfying, it has everything to recommend it.

The racist viewpoint is not inherently unreasonable. Indeed, if one looks no deeper than the surface, it is almost at every point confirmed. Those who subscribe to the racist viewpoint usually have a deep emotional investment in it; and for this, among other reasons, when challenged, the racist is liable to react with all those defenses designed to maintain him in his beliefs. This is the principal reason why questions of "race" are so seldom discussed in an atmosphere uncharged with emotion. And this is why Mississippi and Alabama, for example, are terrorist states.

Studies of individuals to whom racism is a congenial way of thinking and behaving have been most helpful in enabling us to understand some of the things that must be done if racism is ever to be reduced to manageable proportions.[1]

PHYSICAL AND BEHAVIORAL TRAITS

It requires to be said at once that, contrary to the racist claim, there exists no linkage whatever between the genetic bases for the development of physical traits and those genes which influence the expression of behavioral traits. The manner in which the idea of the linkage

[1] See T. W. Adorno, E. Frenkel-Brunswik, D. J. Levinson, and R. Nevitt Sanford, *The Authoritarian Personality* (New York: Harper, 1950); Nathan W. Ackerman and Marie Jahoda, *Anti-Semitism and Emotional Disorder* (New York: Harper, 1950); James G. Martin, *The Tolerant Personality* (Detroit: Wayne State University Press, 1964).

between physical and behavioral traits comes about is easy to understand. As Professor Kenneth Mather has recently put it:

> Many non-European peoples, especially savages, have been regarded as genetically inferior because their level of social development was below that of the European, and this view has drawn strength from these people's obvious genetical departures from the European in colour and physical characteristics. The existence of one genetical difference makes it easier to impute another. The falsity of such an argument is self-evident. Since genes can recombine, their effects can be reassociated, so that the differences in the genetic determinants of one character do not imply differences in the determinants of another.[2]

However, even though physical and behavioral traits are not genetically linked, the possibility remains that the distribution of genes permitting a high development of intelligence may be greater in some peoples than in others. Whether this is linkage or not, it is what racists claim.

[2] Kenneth Mather, *Human Diversity* (Edinburgh: Oliver & Boyd, 1964).

This claim may or may not be true. No one is in a position to say that it is either true or false. But what scientists are in a position to say is that there is no evidence whatever to support the racist claim, and that there exists a great deal of evidence serving to disprove it.

Literally thousands of volumes have been written on the subject, and it would be a great boon if we could have them all collected in a single institute for the study of "race." It is an interesting commentary on ourselves that while we have scores of institutes for the study of cancer, we do not have a single institute devoted to the study of this cancer of the mind, namely, racism. We do not yet seem to understand that pathogenic ideas can be quite as dangerous as pathogenic microorganisms, and that the study of the epidemiology of pathogenic ideas is at least as important as the study of the epidemiology of physical disease vectors.[3]

[3] See Frederick E. Thorne, "The Attitudinal Pathoses," *Journal of Clinical Psychology*, V (1949), 1–21; "The Frustration-Anger-Hostility States: A New Diagnostic Classification," *Journal of Clinical Psychology*, IX (1953), 334–339;

THE ORIGIN OF HUMAN VARIETY

It is generally agreed among students of the evolution of man that all men have originated from a common stock and belong to the same species, *Homo sapiens*. In spite of a recent attempt to show that man originated from *Homo erectus* not once but five times, and then that each of the five evolutes independently evolved into *Homo sapiens*, most authorities reject this theory and consider that *Homo sapiens* evolved only once, and that the different so-called "races" simply represent the adaptive responses to the different challenges of the environments in which these different peoples or so-called "races" originating from a common stock found themselves. As Professor Theodosius Dobzhansky has pointed out, "The specific unity of mankind was maintained throughout its history by gene flow due to migrations and the process for which the word 'genosorption' [that is, the process whereby the genes of one

and "Epidemiological Studies of Chronic Frustration-Hostility-Aggression States," *American Journal of Psychiatry*, CXIII (1957), 717–721.

51

population are incorporated into the gene pool of another] is suggested. Excepting through such gene flow, repeated origins of the same species are so improbable that this conjecture is not worthy of serious consideration; and given a gene flow, it becomes fallacious to say that a species has originated repeatedly, and even more fallacious to contend that it has originated five times, or any other number above one."[4]

Reference is made to this matter here because Dr. Carleton S. Coon, the proponent of the theory of the fivefold origin of *Homo sapiens*, has suggested that Negroes were the last of the subspecies or "races" of *Homo erectus* to be transformed into *Homo sapiens*.[5] Since the white man, it is alleged according to this theory, was the earliest to evolve, he has evolved the most; and, of course, the Negro, according to

[4] Theodosius Dobzhansky, "Genetic Entities in Human Evolution," in S. L. Washburn (ed.), *Classification and Human Evolution* (New York: Viking Fund Publications in Anthropology), XXXVII (1963), p. 361.

[5] Carleton S. Coon, *The Origin of Races* (New York: Knopf, 1962).

Coon, having evolved the last, has therefore evolved the least.

This viewpoint has brought gladness to the hearts of racists, and the most vocal among them have already begun to make the most of it. It therefore needs to be said here with all the authority we can muster that there is not the slightest ground for believing that the Negro was the last to evolve into *sapiens* man, that the evidence accepted by most authorities is that all so-called "races" of man evolved as *sapiens* only once, and that the physical differences peoples exhibit came into being after, and not before, they attained the *sapiens* state—in short, that Negroes have at least as long a genetic history as other peoples.[6]

Coon bases his argument that the Negroes were the last of the *sapiens* varieties to evolve on the most hopeless kind of negative evidence. We are simply wanting in any kind of evidence that would enable us to trace the origins of the Negro, or for that matter of any other variety

[6] C. Loring Brace and M. F. Ashley Montagu, *Man's Evolution* (New York: Macmillan, 1965).

of man. The fact that to Coon "Negroes and Pygmies appeared as if out of nowhere" constitutes no more than a statement of our ignorance. Unfortunately, a man who speaks from negative evidence is frequently tempted to substitute his opinions for what he doesn't know. The opinions of such a man are often likely to embody his prejudices; and as such, they are as often of no more value than those of the man in the street.

Those who believe that by pointing out the danger of falling into such errors to those who have committed them, they will thereby be likely to earn the others' undying gratitude are likely to be gravely disappointed.[7] But for those who have not yet fallen into error there remains the possibility of a more gratifying experience. As Plutarch said, "It is a thing of no great difficulty to raise objections against another man's oration—nay, it is a very easy matter—but to produce another in its place is a work entirely

[7] See Theodosius Dobzhansky and Ashley Montagu, "Two Views on Coon's *Origin of Races*," *Current Anthropology*, IV (1963), 360–367.

54

troublesome."[8] And, indeed, it is. But let us attempt it.

If, then, as all the evidence indicates, man originated from a single stock, how is the variety which he presents to be accounted for? In broad outline the answer to that question is as follows: As the result of the migration of individuals and families away from the common *sapiens* homelands, and the long continued isolation of the migrants from the parent and similar related groups reproductively isolated from one another, the inherent variability of the genetic system in random manner produced in the course of time certain patternings of genes differing from those exhibited by the other groups. Furthermore, living in different environments, some under the unremitting action of intense sunlight, and others in areas of reduced sunlight, those individuals possessing genes that would enable them to respond in adaptation to the challenges of the environment would be more likely to leave a larger

[8] Plutarch, *Of Hearing.*

progeny to perpetuate the group than those not possessing the necessary adaptive fitness.

This, in a few words is the explanation for the differences that characterize the varieties of mankind—an explanation which for this and the many other traits that cannot be dealt with here it would take volumes to treat of adequately.[9] The evolutionary factors I have implicitly referred to are migration, isolation, genetic drift, mutation, culture, hybridization, social selection, and natural selection.

We know that migration followed by isolation and the random fixation of mutations (genetic drift) have been constant factors in man's evolutionary history. The permanent change in the structure of a gene leading to a physiological alteration in its effects, that is, mutation, we know to occur in every living thing. We know, also, that mutations favorable to the life of the organism in any environment are likely to be perpetuated, as, for example, mutations for heavy pigment in the skin in high sunlight

[9] See Brace and Montagu, *Man's Evolution.*

56

areas, and lesser amounts of pigment in organisms living in low sunlight areas. We know also that after a time, isolated populations tend to meet and hybridize, and that this, too, has been a factor in the evolution of the physical differences characterizing so-called "races." Such factors and their interpretation are sufficient to account for the physical differences existing between such populations.

But what of the operation of those factors that may have been responsible for the production of mental differences? The answer to that question is by far the most interesting. We may turn to it at once.

Man's principal means of adapting himself to the environment is culture. By culture may be understood the man-made part of the environment—man's knowledge, beliefs, arts, crafts, customs, tools, and habits acquired as a member of society. By means of his culture man is not only able to control his environment, but also to change the pressures of natural selection and thus influence his evolution physically as well as culturally.[10] Because culture has been man's chief means of adapting himself to whatever environments he has found himself in, the cultural challenges of the environment have throughout the whole of man's evolutionary history been virtually of the same kind. For throughout the entire period of the two million years of man's evolutionary history, with the exception of the last twelve thousand years or so, he was a food-gatherer and hunter, living in very small groups, and subject to much the same stresses, strains, and challenges, and called upon everywhere in consequence to make much the same responses to those challenges in order to survive. The challenges were such that the most adaptively valuable traits he could develop would have been plasticity, educability, malleability, flexibility, the ability to adapt himself to rapidly changing conditions rather than to specialize in any one ability, the ability to respond rather than to react to the challenges of the environment. Indeed, this is how, we have every

[10] See Ashley Montagu (ed.), *Culture and the Evolution of Man* (New York: Oxford University Press, 1962).

good reason to believe, this made-over ape became a man: by abandoning his specialized traits, his instinctive predispositions, and becoming increasingly more educable.

When we study societies at the food-gathering–hunting stage of development—economies that parallel those of our more remote ancestors—we find that everywhere in such societies the traits that are most prized in the individual are his plasticity, his educability, and his cooperativeness. It is the malleable individual who is most highly esteemed, and in all societies at this economic level, if we must have one word to define it, it is plasticity, flexibility, that is at a premium. Flexibility of response to different challenges of the environment, physical and cultural, is much more likely to have enjoyed a selective advantage over any tendency toward predetermined reactions. Problem-solving and the ability to profit from experience, that is, intelligence, and emotional and temperamental resilience have been at a high premium in all societies. And in every society those persons were and are most favored who show

59

wisdom, maturity of judgment, the ability to get along with others, and adaptability.

This capacity for plasticity, flexibility, of behavior has been favored by natural and social selection at all times and in all societies in the uniquely social environments in which man has evolved. It is therefore highly improbable that there has been any significant genetic differentiation in the course of man's evolution for any special traits or for capacities that would genetically influence in any significant way the expression of behavior. What has been at a premium in the evolution of man has been plasticity, flexibility, educability, adaptability, and not any form of specialization, unless it may be said, as I think it may, that man has specialized in nonspecialization, that is, that he has specialized in plasticity, in versatility of capacity for response.

For these very cogent reasons, therefore, it is highly probable that the mental capacities of mankind, allowing for the wide range of individual variability, are everywhere much the same. One may go even further and say that on the basis of the observed facts, and considering the wide range of variability that characterizes human beings, the actual differences in mental capacity existing between peoples are likely to be smaller than the differences one is likely to find existing between the members of the same people. The selective pressures for behavioral response to which human beings have been everywhere subjected during the course of their evolution have in all societies been nondifferential selection for educability, that is, for the capacity to modify one's behavior under the influence of experience and reasoning. This selective pressure has had the effect of working upon all human beings in very much the same way and endowing them all, within a wide range of variability, with similar genotypes (genetic constitutions) for behavioral adaptability.

Furthermore, intelligence, from the genetic standpoint, is not so much a product of major genes, that is, of single genes producing a large effect, but rather of polygenes, that is, of many genes each of which produces a small individual

61

quantitative effect. This being the case, it is highly improbable that differences in intelligence would have been brought about in the small separated populations of man by genetic drift. This would require the assumption of so many correlated changes in positive-acting or negative-acting genes as to render such an effect quite out of the question.

In short, the evolutionary facts indicate that the mental capacities of human beings in different populations called "races" are so much alike that for all practical purposes we can assume that given the adequate opportunities, the members of any one group could, with the same or similar frequencies, achieve whatever the members of any other group with the adequate opportunities have achieved. Wherever it has been possible to put this hypothesis to the test, it has been supported by the findings.[11]

But the racists at once raise the question, and others who are not racists may very reasonably

[11] For the evidence, see M. F. Ashley Montagu, *Man's Most Dangerous Myth: The Fallacy of Race* (4th ed.; Cleveland and New York: World Publishing Co., 1964).

raise the same question: Why is it that after one hundred years of emancipation and years of schooling and college for Negroes, there have been so few Negroes who have achieved distinction in the fields in which whites have accomplished so much?

Insofar as Negro achievement in Africa is concerned, this can speak for itself.[12] The Negro peoples of Africa achieved everything they needed to achieve in order to survive in the physical and cultural environments in which they lived. With the tremendous changes to which the peoples of Africa have been exposed during the last hundred years, and the attainment of independence by most of them, as these matters go it ought not to take too long before they are able to demonstrate what they are capable of doing. It took the English over a thousand years after the Roman occupation to get up steam. It is probable that the African peoples will generate it in less time than that.

[12] See Basil Davidson, *The African Past* (Boston: Little, Brown & Co., 1964).

What, then, of the Negro in America; why has he not achieved more than he has?

I believe the simplest and the soundest answer to that question is that the Negro in America has never been afforded the kind of opportunities necessary for accomplishment of any distinction.

The case is exactly parallel with that of women. Up to the first decade of the twentieth century women were the "inferior race" of the masculine world. Everything that has been said about so-called "inferior races" has been said about women. Their brains were small, their intelligence limited, their emotions undisciplined, and they were obsessed by sex. The facts are quite otherwise: Relative to body weight women have larger brains than men, all the tests and everyday experience shows that women are more intelligent than men, that they are in far better condition in the use of their emotions than men, and that it is men, not women, who are obsessed with sex. However, through the distorting-glass of prejudice the whole world is seen awry, and, of course, one's own wide-warped creations are seen as straight.[13]

But now that women are increasingly being afforded opportunities that were formerly withheld from them, they are accomplishing the kind of things that bigots and others, even some women themselves, formerly maintained were quite beyond the intellectual reach of the so-called weaker sex. Women are not the weaker sex. They are the constitutionally stronger sex. Men are muscularly more powerful, and for that reason men have too often chosen to depend upon brawn rather than brain. But man is a myth-making animal, and dearly loves his myths when they support him in what he wants to believe; and he will gladly die in their defense, combatting the truths which would show his myths to be false.

The Negro in America has for three hundred years been isolated from the mainstream of American culture and segregated, like a sequestrum on the body politic, from virtually all

[13] See Gordon Allport, *The Nature of Prejudice* (Cambridge, Mass.: Addison-Wesley, 1953).

THE IDEA OF RACE

opportunity to enjoy the right even to the
feeling that he was a man like other men. On
the contrary, he has been made to feel that he
was distinctly not like other men; that he was
of a different kind; that he was stupid, benighted, degraded, incapable of accomplishing
what his "superiors" have accomplished, and
therefore not worthy of having wasted on him
the kind of social facilities, housing, and edu-
cation to which his "superiors," by their difference in quality, were the natural heirs.

I believe that no one can understand what it
means to be a Negro in America until he awak-
ens one morning with a black skin and then
attempts to live his life as an ordinary human
being. John Howard Griffin has conveyed something of what such a life is like in his book
Black Like Me.[14] But one really has to be a
Negro to receive the full impact of what it
means to be a Negro in America—anywhere in
America, and not merely in Mississippi or the
states of those noble representatives of white

[14] Boston: Houghton Mifflin Co., 1961.

66

American Protestant Christianity, Governors Wallace and Faubus. Everywhere in America the Negro has been the victim of the white man's prejudice against him. The American Negro has been oppressed, lynched, murdered, terrorized, deprived of his legal and social rights, segregated, and impoverished in every way. Obstacles of every kind have been placed in his path, and so far as his aspirations for anything better are concerned, he has been made to feel that the white man's floor is the black man's ceiling. All this adds up to what may be called the "degradation effect." Negroes have been made to feel so degraded for so long that most of them have come to believe that within the framework of what is permissible to them in American society there is very little that they can aspire to, especially in the realm of intellectual achievement.

It is not surprising that on the whole Negroes do not do as well as whites on whatever it is that so-called intelligence tests are supposed to measure. Whites would not, and in fact do not, do as well as Negroes on the same intelligence tests

67

when they have been socialized in Negro-like environments, as in the South, and the Negroes have enjoyed better social conditions, as the World War I army tests and later similar tests show.[15]

Achievements imply opportunities, and they must be more than token or occasional opportunities. In addition, they must be opportunities in a context of the freedom to deliberate and to choose in an environment which is permissive and holds out the promise of being able to realize one's capacities, and they must be opportunities that are open-endedly available to the whole population and not merely to an occasional individual.

Where in America at any time in its history have there been such conditions for the Negro? The answer is, nowhere, and at no time. And that is, almost certainly, the answer to the question why the Negro has not accomplished anything comparable to the white man's achievements.

[15] Ashley Montagu, *Race, Science and Humanity* (Princeton: Van Nostrand Co., 1963), pp. 84–113.

Let it be noted that in those areas in which self-taught skills are involved—in music, both vocal and instrumental, in the dance, in composition, in the theatre, in sports, in athletics, in oratory, and in literature—American Negroes have achieved outstanding successes. But these are areas in which a broad permissiveness exists in some parts of the country, and in which it takes no elaborate preparation to become skilled. Such skills are not dependent upon training in good schools and a long and expensive college and postgraduate training with the promise of a good berth at the end of it. The Negro's schools are usually shockingly inferior, and his encouragements to continue schooling beyond high school are diminishingly small. It is cruelly and utterly unrealistic to think of the Negro, whether child or adult, as under any possible circumstances being seriously enough interested in matters intellectual to consider persisting in such an interest. The discouragements are simply too great.

White Americans owe the American Negro an incalculable reparation for the crimes they

69

have committed against him and the damage
they have done him. We should all put a levy
upon ourselves, in both time and money, to
make reparation for our past misdeeds. Let us
stop assuming that we know what the Negro
or any other man is by nature. Let us begin to
understand that a man's nature is not what he
is born with, but what we make of what he is
born with. What man has made of man, is man's
nature, and that nature can be changed according to the pattern to which it is tailored in
custom-made society. What white Christian
America has made of the American Negro is
so terrible, so constant an accusation, that being
unable to face the guilt with which we are daily
confronted, we do our best to sequester it, to
"keep the Negro in his proper place" and thus
out of mind. But guilt feelings are not easily
erased. The problem, the sickness, remains, and
it is only worsened by the devices and rationalizations and iniquities of racists. Nor will that
problem be solved by the disproof of the racist's
unfounded claims by confronting him with the
facts. Nevertheless, the facts have a certain

70

value, if for no other reason than that they serve to show how ridiculous the racist's interpretations of the facts are. Facts, of course, do not speak for themselves, but are at the mercy of whoever seeks to juggle them to whatever end he sees fit.

One of the unchanging devices of the racist is to cite a fact and then proceed to interpret its meaning according to his own desire, and with no concern whatever for the additional facts that really give the cited ones their actual meaning. Thus, one of the facts to which the racist is most devoted is that the average size of the Negro brain is smaller than that of the brain of the average white. The average white brain has a volume of about 1400 cubic centimeters, while the average volume of the Negro brain is some 50 cubic centimeters less. The racist inference from this difference is that the Negro is therefore less intelligent by so much.

What the racist never mentions is that the average volume of the brain of Neanderthal man was 1550 cubic centimeters—150 cubic centimeters greater than that of modern whites!

71

Are we to assume, then, that Neanderthal man was 150 cubic centimeters more intelligent than the modern white man? Eskimos have an average brain volume exceeding 1560 cubic centimeters, and so do Mongols. Most American Indians have a larger brain volume than most whites, and interestingly enough, so do some African peoples like the Amahosa, with an average brain volume of 1490 cubic centimeters. One cannot help wondering why such facts are not mentioned by racists when they make their brain-volume–intelligence comparisons. These facts are readily available. Can it be that racists are aware that facts such as these play havoc with their argument?

The truth is that for all living peoples, within the limits of normal variability for brain size— that is, from 850 cubic centimeters to 2000 cubic centimeters and more—brain size has no relation whatever to intelligence. Size, shape, form, weight, volume, number and depth of convolutions, cell number, and the like—none of these factors have any relation whatever to intelligence.

Many a reputation has been lost in the sinuous convolutions of the brain in the attempt to show that they were significantly related to intelligence. There is no such relation whatsoever, in spite of Dr. Carleton S. Coon's recent attempt to suggest, in a manner that has been devastatingly criticized by a number of anthropologists, that such a relationship exists.[16]

It is pointed out by racists that the Negro's extremities are longer than those of whites, the suggestion here being that therefore the Negro more closely resembles the ape than does the

[16] See Nigel Barnicot, "Coon's Theory of Evolution," *The Observer Weekend Review*, XXVI (May 1963); J. S. Birdsell, "The Origin of Human Races," *Quarterly Review of Biology*, XXXVIII (1963), 178–185; Theodosius Dobzhansky, "Possibility That *Homo Sapiens* Developed Independently 5 Times Is Vanishing Small," *Current Anthropology*, IV (1963), 360–367; Theodosius Dobzhansky, "Genetic Entities in Human Evolution"; Ashley Montagu, "What Is Remarkable About Varieties of Man Is Likenesses, Not Differences," *Current Anthropology*, IV (1963), 360–367; W. J. Crenshaw, Jr., "Direction of Human Evolution: A Zoologist's View," *Human Biology*, XXXV (1963), 250–262; D. F. Roberts, "Review of *The Origin of Races*," *Human Biology*, XXXV (1963), 443–445.

white man. But the fact is that the ape has shorter lower extremities than man, and that because the Negro's lower extremities are slightly longer than those of the white man, he ought, therefore, to be considered more distantly removed from the ape than the white man! However, the ape's upper extremities are longer than those of man, and since the Negro approaches the ape more closely in that respect, he is in that respect nearer the ape. So the net result is that the comparison cancels itself out into the utter nonsense the inferences drawn from it constitute.

The significant fact is that the general linearity of Negro body-form is the result of the action of ecological conditions to which it constitutes the successful adaptation, following Allen's Rule that limbs, among other protruding parts, of those individuals living in the warmer parts of the species range will, in general, increase in linearity with increase in temperature, and those of populations living in cooler parts of the species range decrease with decrease in temperature. As examples of these ecological relationships we may point to the linear Nilotic Negro, and the comparatively short, squat Eskimo. Here, also, Bergmann's Rule is operative, that is, body size of populations of the species usually increases with decreasing mean temperature of their habitat.

But these are the kinds of facts in which racists have no interest whatever. Perhaps as an example of the ridiculous lengths to which racists can go in their desire to prove the Negro inferior, which is worthy of some sort of prize, reference may be made to the work of the late Charles B. Davenport, member of the National Academy of Sciences, for many years director of the Eugenics Records Office, one of the founders of genetics in the United States, and an important influence in the framing of our racist immigration laws. In a work entitled *Race Crossing in Jamaica*, published by the Carnegie Institution of Washington in 1929 and written by Davenport and published under his name and that of the gatherer of the data on which the book is based, Morris Steggerda, Davenport drew attention to the fact that a certain number

75

of hybrid offspring of white and black admixture exhibited what he called a disharmony of long legs and short arms. "A long-legged, short-armed person has, indeed," he pointed out, "to stoop more to pick up a thing on the ground than one with the opposite combination of disharmony in the appendages."[17]

When one examines the actual measurements, one finds that the arm length of the hybrids is, on the average, six-tenths of a centimeter greater than in the blacks and one and one-tenth centimeters greater than in whites, while the leg length of the hybrids is two-tenths of a centimeter less than in blacks. It is here that the alleged disharmony is found to exist. But the plain fact is that these differences in no way constitute a disharmony of any kind, except in the mind of one who desires to see it as such. From the practical viewpoint of stooping to pick anything up, or in any other way, these differences are of no significance whatever.

[17] Charles B. Davenport and Morris Steggerda, *Race Crossing in Jamaica* (Washington, D. C.: Carnegie Institution, 1929), p. 471.

To what extremes a racist, who was also a respected scientist in other fields, is willing to go to prove the Negro inferior is revealed in the same work by Davenport when he wrote the following astonishing words: "The Blacks seem to do better in simple mental arithmetic and with numerical series than the Whites. They also follow better complicated directions for doing things. It seems a plausible hypothesis, for which there is considerable support, that the more complicated a brain, the more numerous its 'association fibers,' the less satisfactorily it performs the simple numerical problems which a calculating machine does so quickly and accurately."[18]

Even when Negroes do better than whites, their accomplishment must, so to speak, be denigrated and turned into yet another evidence of their inferiority! Needless to say, or perhaps it very much needs to be said, there is no evidence whatsoever that Negroes have a less complicated brain than whites or that they have fewer association fibers.

[18] *Ibid.*, p. 469.

77

The whole notion that there are some peoples who stand closer on the evolutionary scale to apes than do others is utter nonsense. There are no such peoples. The physical differences that characterize the different peoples of the earth represent the expression of adaptations to environments in which they have undergone the major part of their development, plus the action of such processes as hybridization and genetic drift. If white men have a hairiness, hair form, thin lips, and other traits that cause them to resemble apes more closely than do Negroes, it is not because the white man is more apelike than the Negro, but because his and the Negro's evolutionary history have been somewhat different. It may be that some of these traits are not unrelated to the fact that both the Negro and the white have an apish ancestry. If that is so, then what is ape for the one is ape for the other. If the Negro possesses apelike traits, so does the white man, because both have a common ancestry in the ape. The Negro, however, has no more of such traits either quantitatively or qualitatively than does the

78

white man or any other kind of man.

It is easy to magnify differences and to over-look likenesses, even though the differences are few and are vastly outweighed in number by the likenesses. Similarities do not appear to be as susceptible of definition as differences. Both the differences and the likenesses represent the expression of the adaptations of the ancestors of those who exhibit them to the environments in which they underwent evolutionary differentiation. Far from being marks of inferiority, the differences should be regarded as the evidences of man's remarkable adaptability to every challenging variety of environment to which he has been exposed, and which he has so successfully mastered.

The physical and cultural differences exhibited by the peoples of the world should constitute not causes for discrimination but matters for congratulation. If we would learn to respect and value the differences that characterize us, we must learn to acknowledge the similarities that characterize us. We are, each of us, members of a single human family, the family of

79

humanity, and like the members of a family, each with his physical and behavioral uniqueness, each of not less worth because of those differences than the other.

All the talk and research in the world concerning the meaning of the physical and behavioral traits of the peoples of humanity are, in fact, irrelevant to the main consideration at issue. That consideration is the principle that the right to fulfillment depends not upon the presence or absence of certain physical or behavioral traits, but upon the simple fact that by virtue of being born to humanity, every human being has a right to the development and fulfillment of his potentialities as a human being. That is a principle which depends not upon the facts of science, but rests firmly upon the foundation of ethics.

The "race" problem is a problem of ethics. It is a problem in which we are all deeply involved. What we have each to ask ourselves is whether we are going to continue to remain part of the problem or whether we are going to make ourselves part of the solution.

80

III.

The Inadequacies of the Biological Conception of Race

"Races do not exist; classifications of mankind do."
—George A. Dorsey, "Race and Civilization" (in *Whither Mankind*, ed. Charles Beard, 1928).

The social conception of "race" has long been under attack, but with the exception of the criticism by a few scientists, the biological conception of "race" has not come under intensive critical scrutiny until recent years. The biological idea of "race," that is to say, the notion that a species is generally comprised of a number of populations each of which differs from the others in one or more physical and/or behavioral traits or genes, is still widely held among biologists. It constitutes a tenet of faith among most of the older generation of physical anthropologists.

The biological conception of "race" is essentially a population concept, otherwise all individuals, with the exception of identical twins, would constitute separate races, since every individual differs from every other in physical traits, in genes, and in behavioral traits. In fact, the terms "filial population" and "clone" have been applied to each individual born of a single female.[1] Such terms have very definite uses, but it must always be remembered that they are definitional, and so long as they retain some usefulness, their usage is perfectly legitimate. When, however, a term becomes obfuscating, its usage should be discontinued.

Zoological terminology has its origins in Aristotelian sources, passed through the alembic of medieval theological commentators and the classificatory labors of herbalists before the birth of modern science in the seventeenth century. A definition in Aristotelian terms required the statement of the genus, species, properties, differences, and accidental qualities of whatever it was that was being defined so that it could be

[1] J. Gordon Edwards, "A New Approach to Intraspecific Categories," *Systematic Zoology*, III (1954), 1–20.

distinguished from every other thing on earth. As a formal system of definition, the Linnaean method of classifying living things did not spring Minerva-like from Linnaeus' head. It was simply waiting to be adapted to such purposes as Linnaeus put it. It was and is a scheme of great utility, but it was and remains a highly formal system, an attempt to approximate as nearly as possible to the realities of things. The trouble arises when *definitions* begin to be mistaken for *realities*, and the definitions assume a factitious life of their own. This has been a principal difficulty with such terms as "race" or "subspecies," especially when applied to man. It is a difficulty which was already recognized by several acute observers during the eighteenth century. On an earlier page reference has already been made to the criticisms of the concept of "race" originating with Blumenbach and Herder during the last quarter of the eighteenth century. During the nineteenth century, in his magnificent work, *The Natural History of Man*, first published in 1843, the anthropologist John Cowles Prichard concluded

that "the different races of man are not distinguished from each other by strongly marked,
uniform, and permanent distinctions, as are the
several species belonging to any given tribe of
animals. All the diversities which exist are variable, and pass into each other by insensible
gradations; and there is, moreover, scarcely an
instance in which the actual transition cannot
be proved to have taken place."[2]

In an essay published in 1865 Thomas Henry
Huxley decried the loose usage of classificatory
terms, particularly as applied to man. Huxley
wrote, "I speak of 'persistent modifications' or
'stocks' rather than of 'varieties,' or 'species,'
because each of these last well-known terms im-
plies, on the part of its employer, a preconceived
opinion touching one of those problems, the
solution of which is the ultimate object of the
science; and in regard to which, therefore,
ethnologists are especially bound to keep

[2] James Cowles Prichard, *The Natural History of Man*
(London: Ballière, 1843). The quoted passage is from the
4th edition, 1855, p. 644.

their minds open and their judgments freely balanced."[3]

In his presidential address to the Royal Anthropological Institute in 1885, the distinguished zoologist Sir William Henry Flower wrote:

> It cannot be too often insisted on that the various groups of mankind, owing to their probable unity of origin, the great variability of individuals, and the possibility of all degrees of intermixture of races at remote or recent periods of the history of the species, have so much in common that it is extremely difficult to find distinctive characters capable of strict definition, by which they may be differentiated. It is more by the proponderance of certain characters in a large number of members of a group, than by the exclusive or even constant possession of these characters, in each of its members, that the group as a whole may be characterized.[4]

[3] Thomas Henry Huxley, "On the Methods and Results of Ethnology," in *Man's Place in Nature* (London: Scott; New York: Appleton, 1895), pp. 209–210. Originally published in the *Fortnightly Review*, 1865.

[4] William H. Flower, "On the Classification of the Varieties of the Human Species," in *Essays on Museums and Other Subjects Connected with Natural History* (London:

In his widely read book *The Races of Man*, published simultaneously in French and in English in 1900, the French anthropologist Joseph Deniker objected to the term "race" on much the same grounds as Huxley had done. The first few pages of his book are devoted to the demonstration of the difficulty of applying zoological terms to the classification of man. He writes:

> We have presented to us Arabs, Swiss, Australians, Bushmen, English, Siouan Indians, Negroes, etc., without knowing if each of these groups is on an equal footing from the point of view of classification.

> Do these real and palpable groupings represent unions of individuals which, in spite of some slight dissimilarities, are capable of forming what zoologists call "species," "subspecies," "varieties," in the case of wild animals, or "races" in the case of domestic animals? One need not be a professional anthropologist to reply negatively to this question. They are *ethnic groups* formed by vir-

Macmillan, 1898), p. 275. (Address delivered at the anniversary meeting of the Anthropological Institute of Great Britain and Ireland, 27 January 1885.)

86

tue of community of language, religion, social in-
stitutions, etc., which have the power of uniting
human beings of one or several species, races, or
varieties, and are by no means zoological species.[6]

Franz Boas has told how at this period he
was shocked by the formalism of the approaches
to the problems of "race." "We talk glibly," he
wrote, "of races and nobody can give us a definite answer to the question what constitutes a
race."[6] George Dorsey, in 1928, in an admirable
and too little known examination of racist
claims, put the matter in a sentence: "Races do
not exist; classifications of mankind do."[7]

In 1936 Julian Huxley, a biologist, and Alfred Cort Haddon, an anthropologist, combined
forces to examine the biological concept of race
as applied to man and found it wanting. After

[5] Joseph Deniker, *The Races of Man: An Outline of
Anthropology and Ethnography* (London: Scott, 1900),
pp. 2–3.

[6] Franz Boas, "History and Science in Anthropology: A
Reply," *American Anthropologist*, XXXVIII (1936), p. 140.

[7] George A. Dorsey, "Race and Civilization," in Charles
Beard (ed.), *Whither Mankind: A Panorama of Modern
Civilization* (New York: Longmans, Green & Co., 1928), p.
254.

87

considering the evidence, these investigators concluded, "It is very desirable that the term *race* as applied to human groups should be dropped from the vocabulary of science."[8] "Nowhere," they went on to add, "does a human group now exist which corresponds closely to a systematic sub-species in animals, since various original sub-species have crossed repeatedly and constantly. For the existing populations, the non-committal term *ethnic group* should be used."[9] "The essential reality of the existing situation, however, is not the hypothetical sub-species or races, but the *mixed ethnic groups*, which can never be genetically purified into their original components, or purged of the variability which they owe to past crossing. Most anthropological writings of the past, and many of the present fail to take account of this fundamental fact."[10]

[8] Julian S. Huxley and Alfred Cort Haddon, *We Europeans: A Survey of "Racial" Problems* (New York: Harper, 1936), p. 82.

[9] *Ibid.*, p. 108.

[10] *Ibid.*, p. 114.

88

In an essay on "The Concept of Race," published in 1931, the social biologist Lancelot Hogben made what undoubtedly represents the most withering attack on the anthropological concept of "race" ever published. It constitutes a commentary of some sort upon the nature of these things that in the one-third of a century that has elapsed since that brilliant foray was carried out, there is scarcely a reference to be found to it in the whole of the anthropological literature! In this essay Hogben thoroughly demolished the concept of "race" and observed that the "reasonable position for the biologist to adopt would be an attitude of experimental scepticism. Experiment and experiment alone can decide the limits of development imposed by whatever genetic differences distinguish one racial group considered as a fictitious whole from another racial group considered as a fictitious whole."[11]

In 1941 I published a critical examination

[11] Lancelot Hogben, "The Concept of Race," in *Genetic Principles in Medicine and Social Science* (London: Williams & Norgate, 1931; New York: Knopf, 1931), p. 122.

of "The Concept of Race in the Light of Genetics" in which I presented essentially the same ideas as those of my predecessors set out in the foregoing passages, for it was these writings that most influenced my own thinking on "race." In summing up I wrote, "The indictment against the anthropological conception of race is (1) that it is artificial; (2) that it does not agree with the facts; (3) that it leads to confusion and the perpetuation of error, and finally, that for all these reasons it is meaningless, or rather more accurately such meaning as it possesses is false. Being so weighed down with false meaning it were better that the term be dropped altogether than that any attempt should be made to give it a new meaning."[12]

These criticisms were considered extreme, even ridiculous, by most physical anthropologists. Races, it was held, exist, but not the kind of entities that many people understood by the term "race." Therefore, re-education should be

[12] Ashley Montagu, "The Concept of Race in the Human Species in the Light of Genetics," *Journal of Heredity*, XXIII (1941), pp. 243–247.

attempted by establishing the true meaning of "race." It was not the term that required changing, but people's ideas about it. It was a common failing to argue from the abuse of an idea to its total exclusion. It was a subterfuge, an artful dodge, an attempt to deny what was obvious to everyone. And so on.

Such criticisms are still the order of the day. It is not so much that the critics miss the point, as that they insist upon the validity of whatever definition of race they prefer. They then go on to claim that any denial of the conditions described is a denial of the demonstrable facts. But this *is* to miss the point, namely, that while it is usually true that populations differ in one or more genes from one another, it serves no useful purpose to call that fact a matter of "race," especially in the case of man.

All human beings and all human groups differ from one another in one or more genes. That is the fact; and it is also a fact that when such individuals or groups are classed into arbitrary subdivisions called "races," no matter what the criteria for such subdivisions may be,

91

these classifications are still arbitrary and corre-
spond to nothing in reality. What is more important, such arbitrary subdivisions cannot be
regarded as units of evolution either in space
or in time. In the particular case of man the
"races" that have been arbitrarily recognized
run from a few to scores. What is obscured by
such arbitrary definitions of a "race" is the fact,
first, that the very idea of "race" exists only in
the mind of the definer, that it is an abstraction;
second, that it in fact corresponds to nothing in
reality; and third, that it obscures the real
meaning of population variability. In short, the
biological concept of "race" is an obfuscating
one.

This critical view of the biological concept
of "race" found sporadic but increasing expression in the literature of the second quarter of
this century. Thus, Calman, a zoologist, in 1942
suggested that "terms such as 'geographical
race,' 'form,' 'phase,' and so forth, may be useful
in particular instances but are better not used
until some measure of agreement is reached as

to their precise meaning."[13] Kalmus, a geneticist, in 1948 wrote, "A very important term which was originally used in systematics is 'race.' Nowadays, however, its use is avoided as far as possible in genetics."[14] In a later work published in 1957 Kalmus wrote, "It is customary to discuss the local varieties of humanity in terms of 'race.' However, it is unnecessary to use this greatly debased word, since it is easy to describe populations without it."[15] G. S. Carter, a zoologist, in 1951 wrote that the terms " 'race,' 'variety,' and 'form' are used so loosely and in so many senses that it is advisable to avoid using them as infraspecific categories."[16] Ernst Hanhart in 1953 denied that there are any "true races" in man;[17] and Lionel Penrose, a geneti-

[13] W. T. Calman, *Classification of Animals* (New York: Wiley, 1949), p. 14.

[14] H. Kalmus, *Genetics* (London: Pelican Books, 1948), p. 45.

[15] H. Kalmus, *Variation and Heredity* (London: Routledge, 1957), p. 30.

[16] G. S. Carter, *Animal Evolution* (New York: Macmillan, 1951), p. 163.

[17] Ernst Hanhart, "Infectious Diseases," in Arnold Sorsby

cist, in 1952 wrote that he was unable to "see the necessity for the rather apologetic retention of the obsolete term 'race,' when what is meant is simply a given population differentiated by some social, geographical or genetical character, or . . . merely, by a gene frequency peculiarity. The use of the almost mythical concept of race makes the presentation of the facts about the geographical and linguistic groups . . . unnecessarily complicated."[18]

Meanwhile, some biologists had begun to publish extensive critical examinations of the concept of subspecies or race as used by biologists. What had given rise to the revolt against this concept was the literally frightening multiplication of new subspecies that were being "discovered" and published each year, when it was fairly evident that what was being done in most cases was to give subspecific rank to populations of a species varying in some interesting

---

(ed.), *Clinical Genetics* (St. Louis: Mosby, 1953), pp. 252–253.

[18] Lionel Penrose, *Annals of Eugenics*, XVII (1952), 252–253.

but insignificant respects. Some idea of the dimensions of this problem for biologists may be gained from the fact, for example, that each year some ten thousand new species and genera of insects alone are described and named, and each year the number increases.[19]

In 1953 E. O. Wilson and W. L. Brown, Jr., published a careful critical analysis of the subspecies concept. They criticized that concept on the grounds, among others, that

> . . . most taxonomic recognition of subspecies has proceeded on the oversimplified "coadaptive system" concept of the race, which assumes that genetically independent characters will tend to be concordant in their geographical variation. We believe that this assumption has resulted in the establishment of a basic fallacy in the taxonomic method of studying geographical variation. The tendency in this method has been to delimit races on the basis of one or several of the most obvious characters available in preserved material; the remainder of the geographically variable characters are then ignored, or if they are considered at all,

[19] See William Brown, Jr., "An International Taxonomic Register: Preliminary Proposals," *Systematic Zoology,* X (1961), 80–85.

they are analyzed only in terms of the subspecific units previously defined. A slight variation of the procedure is to choose several discordant characters, employ them in combinations of two or three to establish racial limits, and then analyze each character individually in terms of these limits. . . . Because the geographical race has a demonstrably flimsy conceptual basis, it is unfortunate that it has become through the years a deeply rooted taxonomic resort. That the race has become so integral a part of our systematics is due largely to the circumstance that under the more hierarchical-sounding alias "subspecies," it has established itself gradually but ever more firmly as a unit that could and should be dignified with a Latin name.[20]

Many other biologists have in recent years shown how unsoundly the subspecies concept has been applied to various animal groups without necessarily rejecting the concept of subspecies altogether.[21] More recently several of the younger generation of physical anthropologists

[20] E. O. Wilson and William Brown, Jr., "The Subspecies Concept and Its Taxonomic Application," *Systematic Zoology*, II (1953), 97–111.

[21] See note 19.

have begun to draw attention to the inadequacies of the concept of "race" as applied to man.

In June 1962, the physical anthropologist Frank B. Livingstone published a short paper, "On the Non-Existence of Human Races."[22] In that paper he presented several cogent reasons for abandoning the concept of "race" as applied to the living populations of *Homo sapiens*. First among these reasons was that the variability encountered in human populations does not in the least conform to the discrete packages labeled "races"; in short, that there are no races, but only gradients of characters that merge continuously into the characters of other populations, that is, clines. A cline is a character gradient within a series of interlinked populations or populations considered as interlinked, whose members display a gradual and nearly continuous variation of characteristics from one area to another. The realities, indeed, are the clines and not the arbitrarily separated

[22] Frank B. Livingstone, "On the Non-Existence of Human Races," *Current Anthropology*, III (1962), 279–281.

portions of them that various armchair anthropologists and others have chosen to call "races." Livingstone calls, instead, for the active investigation and analysis of clines. The elaborated version of Livingstone's paper is well worth reading, for although it may not say anything that has not been said before, it states the case against the concept of "race" with admirable force and clarity.[23] We shall continue with that indictment in what follows.

TAXONOMY AND DEFINITION

It is possible to arrive at any number of verbally valid concepts by setting up a group of arbitrary criteria and circumscribing them by definition in such a manner that while they apply to verifiable conditions, they nevertheless constitute an arbitrary delimitation of a non-delimitable fluctuating universe. The question is whether such an arbitrary procedure in connection with the delimitation of populations of

[23] For an elaborated version of Livingstone's paper, see Ashley Montagu (ed.), *The Concept of Race* (New York: Free Press, 1964), pp. 46–60.

man serves any useful purpose. I do not think that it does. The difficulty with such a procedure in the case of man is that it obscures what is really going on within the species by rendering static what is dynamic, and by assuming that the difference in the frequency of a gene or genes characterizing different populations thereby renders the populations significantly different entities. This is especially true when these differences are more or less limited to geographically definable areas. A period is put to a flowing sentence where at most a comma belongs. Arbitrary taxonomic punctuation can play just as much havoc with the meaning of biological processes as arbitrary punctuation can in writing.

Taxonomy at the "racial" level in man fails to recognize the realities of the situation. It is procrustean, forcing the facts to fit the definition, rather than fitting the definition to the facts. It is arbitrary. It places unwarranted emphasis on limits, boundaries, and fixation, thus obscuring the fact that human populations are more or less open systems, processual in nature, with shifting and temporary boundaries, if any, presenting more often than not more or less continuous character gradients distinguished not by unchangefulness, but by flux. The realities of the situation are operationally best defined by the clinal relations that exist between the populations of man, and not by the arbitrarily created "racial" ones.

There are ex cathedra, declarative, descriptive, and analytic approaches to the study of the origin and evolution of man. The ex cathedra, declarative, and descriptive approaches have had their day. What calls for development is the analytic approach. It is not enough to describe population gene frequencies. It is much more important to discover what the differences in gene frequency mean. That such differences make it possible to erect boundaries between the populations exhibiting them, or that the likenesses they exhibit necessarily approximate them more closely, are assumptions only too frequently made. The gene frequency differences tell us only that they exist. How they may have come about is a problem almost as difficult of solution as is the historical reconstruction of man's customs.

We know that genes mutate. We also know that human populations or segments of them, both in the prehistoric and in the historic periods, have wandered and interbred with the members of other populations. Mutation and migration have, on the whole, proceeded in a pretty random manner, in a sort of Brownian movement. In attempting to reconstruct the biological history of populations, the best that can be done (as the physicist does for his atoms) is to achieve a statistically accurate generalized idea of what actually occurs or has occurred. The clinal analysis of human populations achieves a much nearer approach to the processual realities than does the attempt at racial analysis.

Traditional racial classifications are outmoded and should, when an adequate clinal analysis of human populations has been achieved, be replaced by a scheme which represents the living realities.

Wilson and Brown found that the genetic

101

variation in the local populations of the wide-ranging species they studied was discordant, that is, the variation in genetic traits was uncorrelated with geography; the variability of one character did not reflect the variability of another, although among relatively geographically separated but related species (allopatric species) such correlations are usually found. Hence, it is possible to recognize such related species as discrete units, as distinct species, but it is not possible to make such discriminations of a single species into such discrete units. The variation within a species is the result of causes very different from those which produce variation between species. For example, while specific differences may be produced by mutation, isolation, and genetic drift, the differences within the populations or clines of a species may have been produced by the processes of repeated migrations and hybridization, which have had the effect of producing the clinal effects that one observes between human populations. This is the reason why the study of the clinal frequencies of genetic traits are of such great inter-

102

est—because they will enable us to reconstruct something of the biological history of each trait, rather than to obscure that discovery by treating them as an amalgam of concordant traits called "race."

Wilson and Brown pointed out that the naming of subspecies "tends to be an inefficient and misleading method. It is felt that geographical variation should be analyzed first in terms of genetically independent characters, which would then be employed synthetically to search for possible racial groupings."[24] In truth if the meaning of human diversity is ever to be understood, it will not be achieved by any attempt to consider the aggregation of traits which any taxonomist chooses to define as a "race," but rather by the study of single traits as such. As Brace[25] and Brace and Montagu[26] have recently pointed out, neither the study of gene frequency

[24] Wilson and Brown, "The Subspecies Concept and Its Taxonomic Application," p. 110.

[25] C. Loring Brace, "On the Race Concept," *Current Anthropology*, V (1964), 313–320.

[26] C. Loring Brace and M. F. Ashley Montagu, *Man's Evolution* (New York: Macmillan, 1965), pp. 267–326.

distributions nor the study of populations or "races" will throw much light upon the processes responsible for the traits in which we are interested, since such traits in many cases are not limited by genetic or population boundaries. What is important in the study of human diversity are the factors that have influenced the development of each trait itself. This would necessitate the study of the selective and adaptive factors that have been operative in each case. As an illustration of what can be achieved this way, the recent work on sickle-cell anemia may be cited.

Sickle-cell anemia is a disorder characterized by episodes of pain, ulcers of the legs, bossing and towering of the skull, and symptoms of a rheumatoid type. It is a hereditary disorder of the red blood cells, which assume elongated and curved or sickle-shaped forms, evidence of abnormal destruction of the blood. The immediate cause of the sickling phenomenon and of the hemolysis of sickle-cell anemia is the replacement of part or all of the normal hemoglobin of the red blood corpuscles by a form of

104

hemoglobin which, in the reduced state, has a very low solubility and crystallizes inside the cell, causing its breakdown. The sickle-cell trait carrier (who is usually heterozygous) has less than half of this abnormal kind of hemoglobin S, while most of the sickle-cell anemics, who are usually homozygous, have nearly 100 per cent of it, usually with some of the fetal type (F) of hemoglobin as well.

The gene responsible for sickling is identifiable with one of an alternative pair of alleles (allelic genes are situated at corresponding loci in a pair of chromosomes), as Hb^A and Hb^s, where Hb^A is the gene controlling the normal hemoglobin molecule, and Hb^s is the gene controlling the deficient hemoglobin S of sickle-cell anemia. In normal unaffected persons there is a complete absence of the deficient gene Hb^s and two doses of the normal allele are present, as $Hb^A Hb^A$. In sickle-cell anemia the somatic cells carry two doses of the sickle-cell gene, as $Hb^s Hb^s$, and exhibit a complete absence of the normal gene. In the heterozygous state $Hb^A Hb^s$ there is a 40 per cent deficiency in the hemoglobin, the 60 per cent normal hemoglobin being sufficient to protect most heterozygotes against a full expression of sickle-cell anemia. The sickling gene is therefore seen to behave as a dominant, which in the heterozygous condition may not produce more than a mild anemia, but in the homozygous state produces full-fledged sickle-cell anemia. The facts are set out below:

Allele	Allele	Condition		Hemoglobin
Hb^A	Hb^A	Normal	A	100% Normal
Hb^A	Hb^S	Sickle-trait carrier	A	55–75% Normal
			S	25–45% Sickling type
Hb^S	Hb^S	Sickle-cell anemia	S	80–100% Sickling type

The sickling trait is most prevalent in areas where malaria is common, and it is now clear that sickling is an adaptive trait directly related to the malarial environment. In 1954 Allison[27] examined the children of a small African village and found that 46 per cent of the nonsicklers were infected with malaria, as against only 28 per cent of the sicklers. Furthermore,

[27] A. C. Allison, "Protection Afforded by the Sickle-Cell Trait Against Subtertian Malarial Infection," *British Medical Journal*, I (1954), 290–294.

the non-sicklers tended to suffer from malaria in a severe form. Allison innoculated 15 adult sicklers and 15 adult non-sicklers with malarial parasites. Fourteen of the non-sicklers came down with malaria, but only two of the sicklers contracted the disease. These findings have been corroborated by many other workers, and it is now evident that the sickle-cell trait[28] confers real advantages *upon the heterozygous carrier against malaria.* The persistence of the sickle-cell trait, then, would be a result of the balance between the pressure of malaria, which tends to increase the frequency of the gene, and that of sickle-cell anemia, which tends to eliminate it. The AS heterozygotes have a much better chance of surviving and leaving progeny behind them than the AA hemoglobin homozygotes, and certainly considerably greater than the SS hemoglobin homozygotes, most of whom die in early childhood; hence, the advantages possessed by the heterozygotes counterbalance

[28] The *sickle-cell trait* refers to the heterozygous carrier trait. *Sickle-cell anemia* or *sicklemia* refers to the homozygous full expression of the disorder.

107

the disadvantages of the homozygotes, a situation known as *balanced polymorphism*. Balanced polymorphism refers to the fact that when the adaptive value of the heterozygote is greater than that of the homozygotes, natural selection will act to preserve a balanced distribution of the genes involved.

The increased resistance of the heterozygotes, it should be stated, is principally due to one type of malaria, the malignant tertian type caused by the *Plasmodium falciparum*. The resistance of the heterozygote is probably due to the fact that this parasite is better able to grow on hemoglobin A than on hemoglobin B.

In an admirable study of the ecology of the sickle-cell gene, Livingstone[29] in 1958 showed how the distribution of the sickle-cell gene came about in West Africa as a consequence of the interaction between selection and gene flow (gene flow refers to the process of gene move-

[29] Frank B. Livingstone, "Anthropological Significance of Sickle-Cell Gene Distribution in West Africa," *American Anthropologist*, LX (1958), 533–562.

ment as a result of both migration and hybridization).

In plotting the distribution of the sickle-cell gene in West Africa, it is observed that the higher frequencies are generally to be found in the south, there being some indication of a north-south gradient. *Plasmodium falciparum* malaria follows a similar gradient. However, there are many highly malarious regions of West Africa in which sickling is of low incidence.

Correlating languages with the distribution of sickling, the indications are, on the whole, that the tribes with a low incidence of sickling are probably the indigenous tribes of West Africa who have been forced back into such areas as Portuguese Guinea and Eastern Liberia, where they have been somewhat isolated. It is only in contemporary times that the sickle-cell gene is being introduced to these tribes.

Since agriculture is not more than 6,000 years old in Africa, there is some reason to believe that the slash-and-burn agriculture practiced is related to the complex epidemiology of malaria

109

in West Africa, and to the selective advantage of the sickle-cell gene. The major vector of malaria is the mosquito *Anopheles gambiae*. The only places in which *A. gambiae* cannot breed are: (1) very shaded water, (2) water with a strong current, (3) brackish water, and (4) very alkaline or polluted water. In a tropical rain forest there would be few places in which *A. gambiae* could breed, the trees effectively shading the ground, and the absorbent humus leaving very few stagnant pools. It is only when man cuts down the forest that *A. gambiae* is provided with an abundance of breeding places. The soil loses its humus and becomes laterized. Virtually impervious to water, the soil now holds it in puddles. Further breeding places are provided by the village settlement in the thatch of its huts and in its abundant refuse.

Hunting populations do not destroy the forest, and exhibit a very low incidence of malaria. The Pygmies of the Ituri Forest are a good example. They are said to suffer from malaria, and are known to exhibit lower frequencies of the sickle-cell gene than surrounding popula-

110

tions, presumably having acquired this gene by admixture with their Negro neighbors.

It would seem, then, that the spread of slash-and-burn agriculture has been responsible for the spread of the selective advantage of the sickle-cell gene, and therefore the sickle-cell gene represents a comparatively recent genetic response to a disease which, in certain parts of the world, at least, has been influencing the evolution of man.

Studies such as these tell us more about the ways in which environmental pressures, and the ways in which these are produced by man's cultural activities, serve to produce evolutionary change than an infinity of gene-frequency studies or any number of descriptions of "races" could ever possibly do. The important thing to note is that such evolutionary changes are not bounded by population or genetic limits.

Another valuable study of a similar kind is Brace's work on the development of the overbite in man. Most readers of this book will have upper front teeth that bite over the lower front teeth. This is a very recent evolutionary devel-

111

opment, and among the modern Eskimo we can actually observe it in process of occurring as these people become addicted to the grain foods introduced by the white man. The edge-to-edge bite was characteristic of all human beings until the food-producing revolution. The edge-to-edge bite is most useful in cutting and manipulating meat and in the use of the front teeth as tools for other purposes. With the advent of the ground-grain-powdered grinding-stone diet of the Neolithic, the overbite first made its appearance. It is significant that among hunting peoples the edge-to-edge bite still prevails.[30] Thus, what had long been assumed to be genetically determined structural and functional traits are shown to be almost certainly due to environmental factors and to have no relation whatever to genetic or "racial" factors. Illuminating discoveries of these kinds are quite beyond the possibility of achievement by the

[30] C. Loring Brace, "Cultural Factors in the Evolution of the Human Dentition," in Ashley Montagu (ed.), *Culture and the Evolution of Man* (New York: Oxford University Press, 1962), 343–354.

traditional approaches to the study of "race."

The hierarchical manner of thinking peculiar to taxonomists has frequently disabled them from perceiving that the hierarchies they have created are artifacts of their imaginations, and that hierarchies do not exist in nature. The dangers inherent in hierarchical thinking are several, among them being the error of taking the abstraction for reality, and the further error of continuous creation of descending units or categories of classification. Thus, if there are phyla, classes, orders, families, subfamilies, genera, and species, then, it is reasoned, there must be categories continuously lower, subspecies or "races," for example. There is, however, neither "must" nor necessity here, unless one becomes the victim of the thing one has created, in this case a taxonomic system not only unreflective of the actual conditions, but serving to obscure them. As Ehrlich and Holm have pointed out, such taxonomic approaches have led, among other things, "to the mistaken assumption that arbitrary racial subdivisions of *Homo sapiens* can be considered as evolution-

113

ary units in space and time."[31] And as these authors and others have said, without the necessary genetic study there is no basis in fact for assuming that any population or taxonomic group constitutes an evolutionary unit. "Discussions of the biological origins and characteristics of subjectively determined races (e.g., Coon, 1963), based exclusively, as they must be, on evolutionary misconceptions, are useful only for strengthening culturally determined prejudices against groups which have reality only in a social, rather than a biological sense."[32]

One of the absurd misconceptions invented by the creators of biological "races" is the notion that "crossing" or "hybridization," or still worse, "miscegenation,"[33] leads to "mongreliza-

[31] Paul R. Ehrlich and Richard W. Holm, *The Process of Evolution* (New York: McGraw-Hill Book Co., 1963); and "A Biological View of Race," in Ashley Montagu (ed.), *The Concept of Race*, p. 171.

[32] *Ibid.*, p. 175.

[33] A reprehensible word originally created as a joke by its inventors, and now carrying with it the pejorative meanings of a "mistake," "a mesalliance," and the like. Ashley Montagu, *Man's Most Dangerous Myth: The Fallacy of Race*

tion." This myth has been exploded many times; nevertheless, it remains the theme song of racists. The fact is that not only has gene exchange between human populations been the rule, much to the benefit of the human species, but there does not exist a single iota of evidence which would even remotely suggest that such gene exchange has ever proved detrimental. On the contrary, the evidence points strongly in the opposite direction, that gene exchange has been an important factor in the creative evolution of man.[34]

Evolutionary change is a dynamic process, not a static one, and that constitutes yet another reason why the idea of a "race" as a group of similar individuals is quite hopeless, for such an artificially created entity would be incapable of change, being hardened immodifiably by the criteria of the taxonomist's preserving-spirit.

(4th ed.; Cleveland and New York: World Publishing Co., 1964), pp. 400–401.

[34] Jean Hiernaux, "The Concept of Race and the Taxonomy of Mankind," in Ashley Montagu (ed.), *The Concept of Race*, pp. 28–45.

As Hiernaux has remarked, "In each generation [such a construct] will consist of an artificial grouping of people who happen to share
a given constellation of characters,"[35] and forever afterward must exhibit that constellation
of characters. The congeries of erroneous ideas
involved in such thinking about what is essentially variable, namely, human variation, should
be obvious.

The truth should be recognized that not all
things are capable of classification, and that
attempted classifications of man beyond the species level cannot be accomplished in the traditional manner, if at all. The materials are too
variable for such classifications ever to be possible. And as Hiernaux has said, "Unclassifiabil-
ity seems to me inherent in the modalities of
human variability."[36] And, indeed, as Hiernaux
concluded:

From whatever viewpoint one approaches the
question of the applicability of the concept of
race to mankind, the modalities of human varia-

[35] *Ibid.*, p. 38.
[36] *Ibid.*, pp. 44–45.

116

bility appear so far from those required for a co-herent classification that the concept must be considered of very limited use. In my opinion, to dismember mankind into races as a convenient approximation requires such a distortion of the facts that any usefulness disappears: on the contrary, only the harm done by such practices remains. They tend to force our minds into erroneous channels of thinking, or, if we manage to retain any lucidity, to enter a maze of distinctions and restrictions.

To give up all general racial classifications would mean for anthropology freeing itself from blinkers it has too long worn, and focusing all its energy on its actual goal: the understanding of human variability, as it really is.[37]

[37] *Ibid.*, pp. 43–44.

Bibliography of Sources

ACKERMAN, NATHAN W. AND MARIE JAHODA. *Anti-Semitism and Emotional Disorder.* New York: Harper, 1950.

ADORNO, T. W., E. FRENKEL-BRUNSWIK, J. LEVINSON, AND R. NEVITT SANFORD. *The Authoritarian Personality.* New York: Harper, 1950.

ALLISON, A. C. "Protection Afforded by the Sickle-Cell Trait Against Subtertian Malarial Infection," *British Medical Journal,* I (1954), 290–294.

ARISTOTLE. *The Politics of Aristotle.* Trans. and ed. by Ernest Barker. Oxford: Clarendon Press, 1946.

BARNICOT, NIGEL. "Coon's Theory of Evolution," *The Observer Weekend Review,* XXVI (May 1963).

BENEDICT, RUTH. *Race: Science and Politics.* New York: Viking Press, 1943.

BIRDSELL, J. S. "The Origin of Human Races," *Quarterly Review of Biology,* XXXVIII (1963), 178–185.

BLUMENBACH, JOHANN FRIEDRICH. *De generis humani varietate nativa.* Göttingen, 1775. Trans. by Thomas Bendyshe, *The Anthropological Treatises of Johann Friedrich Blumenbach* (London: Anthropological Society, 1865).

119

BLUNDEVILLE, THOMAS. *The Fower Chiefest Offices Belonging to Horsemanship*. 1580.

BOAS, FRANZ. "History and Science in Anthropology: A Reply," *American Anthropologist*, XXXVIII (1936), 137–141.

BRACE, C. LORING. "Cultural Factors in the Evolution of the Human Dentition." In Ashley Montagu (ed.). *Culture and the Evolution of Man*. New York: Oxford University Press, 1962.

———. "On the Race Concept," *Current Anthropology*, V (1964), 313–320.

BRACE, C. LORING AND M. F. ASHLEY MONTAGU. *Man's Evolution*. New York: Macmillan, 1965.

BROWN, WILLIAM, JR. "An International Taxonomic Register: Preliminary Proposals," *Systematic Zoology*, X (1961), 80–85.

BUFFON, GEORGES LOUIS LECLERC. *Histoire Naturelle*. 44 vols. Paris, 1749–1804. Trans. by William Smellie, *Natural History* (20 vols.; London: Cadell & Davies, 1812).

CALMAN, W. T. *Classification of Animals*. New York: Wiley, 1949.

CARTER, G. S. *Animal Evolution*. New York: Macmillan, 1951.

CICERO. *Letters to Atticus*. Trans. and ed. by E. O. Winstedt. 3 vols. Loeb Classical Library; Cambridge: Harvard University Press, 1920.

COON, CARLETON S. *The Origin of Races*. New York: Knopf, 1962.

CRENSHAW, W. J., JR. "Direction of Human Evolution: A Zoologist's View," *Human Biology*, XXXV (1963), 250–262.

DAVENPORT, CHARLES B. AND MORRIS STEGGERDA. *Race Crossing in Jamaica*. Washington, D. C.: Carnegie Institution, 1929.

DAVIDSON, BASIL. *The African Past*. Boston: Little, Brown & Co., 1964.

DENIKER, JOSEPH. *The Races of Man: An Outline of Anthropology and Ethnography*. London: Scott, 1900.

DOBZHANSKY, THEODOSIUS. "Genetic Entities in Human Evolution." In S. L. Washburn (ed.). *Classification and Human Evolution*. New York: Viking Fund Publications in Anthropology, Vol. XXXVII (1963).

————. "Possibility That *Homo Sapiens* Developed Independently 5 Times Is Vanishingly Small," *Current Anthropology*, IV (1963), 360–367.

DOBZHANSKY, THEODOSIUS AND ASHLEY MONTAGU. "Two Views on Coon's *Origin of Races*," *Current Anthropology*, IV (1963), 360–367.

DORSEY, GEORGE A. "Race and Civilization." In Charles Beard (ed.). *Whither Mankind: A Pano-*

rama of Modern Civilization. New York: Longmans, Green & Co., 1928.

EDWARDS, J. GORDON. "A New Approach to Intraspecific Categories," *Systematic Zoology*, III (1954), 1–20.

EHRLICH, PAUL R. AND RICHARD W. HOLM. "A Biological View of Race." In Ashley Montagu (ed.). *The Concept of Race*. New York: Free Press, 1964.

———. *The Process of Evolution*. New York: McGraw-Hill Book Co., 1963.

FLOWER, WILLIAM H. "On the Classification of the Varieties of the Human Species." In *Essays on Museums and Other Subjects Connected with Natural History*. London: Macmillan, 1898. (Address delivered at the anniversary meeting of the Anthropological Institute of Great Britain and Ireland, 27 January 1885.)

FONER, PHILIP S. *Basic Writings of Thomas Jefferson*. New York: Halcyon House, 1950.

FOXE, JOHN. *Actes and Monuments*. 2 vols. 1570.

FREMANTLE, ANNE (ed.). *The Papal Encyclicals*. New York: New American Library, 1963.

GOLDSMITH, OLIVER. *An History of the Earth and Animated Nature*. 8 vols. 1774.

GWYDIR, WYNNE OF. *History of the Gwydir Family*. 1600.

HANHART, ERNST. "Infectious Diseases." In Arnold Sorsby (ed.). *Clinical Genetics*. St. Louis: Mosby, 1953.

HANKE, LEWIS. *Aristotle and the American Indians*. Chicago: Henry Regnery Co., 1959.

HERDER, JOHANN GOTTFRIED. *Ideen zur Philosophie der Geschichte der Menschheit*. 4 vols. Riga and Leipzig: J. F. Hartknoch, 1784–1791. Trans. by Thomas Churchill, *Outlines of a Philosophy of the History of Man* (London: J. Johnson, 1803).

HIERNAUX, JEAN. "The Concept of Race and the Taxonomy of Mankind." In Ashley Montagu (ed.). *The Concept of Race*. New York: Free Press, 1964.

HOGBEN, LANCELOT. "The Concept of Race." In *Genetic Principles in Medicine and Social Science*. London: Williams & Norgate, 1931; New York: Knopf, 1931.

HUMBOLDT, ALEXANDER VON. *Cosmos: A Sketch of a Physical Description of the Universe*. Trans. by E. C. Otté. 4 vols. London: Bohn, 1849.

HUMBOLDT, WILHELM VON. *Über die Kawi-Sprache auf der Insel Java*. 3 vols. Berlin: Königlichen Akademie der Wissenschaften, 1836.

HUXLEY, JULIAN S. AND ALFRED CORT HADDON. *We Europeans: A Survey of "Racial" Problems*. New York: Harper, 1936.

123

HUXLEY, THOMAS HENRY. "On the Methods and Results of Ethnology." In *Man's Place in Nature*. London: Scott; New York: Appleton, 1895. (Originally published in the *Fortnightly Review*, 1865.)

ISOCRATES. *Panegyricus*. Trans. by George Norlin. 2 vols. Loeb Classical Library; Cambridge: Harvard University Press, 1928.

JEFFERSON, THOMAS. "Notes on the State of Virginia." In Saul K. Padover (ed.). *The Complete Jefferson*. New York: Tudor Publishing Co., 1943.

KALMUS, H. *Genetics*. London: Pelican Books, 1948.
———. *Variation and Heredity*. *London*: Routledge, 1957.

KHALDÛN, IBN. *The Muqaddimah*. Trans. and ed. by Franz Rosenthal. 3 vols. New York: Pantheon Books, 1958.

LIVINGSTONE, FRANK B. "Anthropological Significance of Sickle-Cell Gene Distribution in West Africa," *American Anthropologist*, LX (1958), 533–562.

———. "On the Non-Existence of Human Races," *Current Anthropology*, III (1962), 279–291.

MARTIN, JAMES G. *The Tolerant Personality*. Detroit: Wayne State University Press, 1964.

MATHER, KENNETH. *Human Diversity*. Edinburgh: Oliver & Boyd, 1964.

MONTAGU, ASHLEY. "The Concept of Race in the

Human Species in the Light of Genetics," *Journal of Heredity*, XXIII (1941), 243–247.

——. *Man's Most Dangerous Myth: The Fallacy of Race.* 4th ed. Cleveland and New York: World Publishing Co., 1964.

——. *Race, Science and Humanity.* Princeton: Van Nostrand Co., 1963.

——. "What Is Remarkable About Varieties of Man Is Likenesses, Not Differences," *Current Anthropology*, IV (1963), 360–367.

—— (ed.). *The Concept of Race.* New York: Free Press, 1964.

—— (ed.). *Culture and the Evolution of Man.* New York: Oxford University Press, 1962.

PADOVER, SAUL K. *A Jefferson Profile.* New York, 1956.

PLUTARCH. *Of Hearing.*

PRICHARD, JAMES COWLES. *The Natural History of Man.* London: Ballière, 1843; 4th ed., 1855.

ROBERTS, D. F. "Review of *The Origin of Races*," *Human Biology*, XXXV (1963), 443–445.

ROUSSEAU, JEAN JACQUES. "A Discourse on the Origin of Inequality." In *A Discourse on the Origin of Inequality* and *The Social Contract*. Trans. by G. D. H. Cole. Everyman's Library; New York: E. P. Dutton, 1932.

——. "The Social Contract." In *A Discourse on the*

125

Origin of Inequality and The Social Contract. Trans. by G. D. H. Cole. Everyman's Library; New York: E. P. Dutton, 1932.

TAUT, FRANÇOIS. *Trésor de la langue française.* Ed. Jean Nicot. Paris: P. Doucer, 1600.

TARN, W. W. *Alexander the Great and the Unity of Mankind.* London, 1933.

THORNE, FREDERICK E. "The Attitudinal Pathoses," *Journal of Clinical Psychology,* V (1949), 1–21.

———. "Epidemiological Studies of Chronic Frustration-Hostility-Aggression States," *American Journal of Psychiatry,* CXIII (1957), 717–721.

———. "The Frustration-Anger-Hostility States: A New Diagnostic Classification," *Journal of Clinical Psychology,* IX (1953), 334–339.

WESTERMANN, W. L. "The Slave Systems of Greek and Roman Antiquity," *Memoirs of the American Philosophical Society,* XL (1955), xi–180.

WILSON, E. O. AND WILLIAM BROWN, JR. "The Subspecies Concept and Its Taxonomic Application," *Systematic Zoology,* II (1953), 97–111.

126